women's fitness magazine

Editor Joanna Knight
Sub-Editors Charlotte Cox, Lucy Cheek
Art Director Matt Reynolds
Senior Designer Alexander Whittaker
Editorial Assistant Amanda Khouv
Nutritionist Nicola Shubrook, Dip (NT-CNM)
Personal Trainer Kristoph Thompson
Recipes and recipe photography StockFood
© The Food Media Agency
Photography Shutterstock, Helen McArdle
Workout model Amy Guy, W Athletic,
www.wathletic.com
Digital Production Manager Nicky Baker

MANAGEMENT
MagBook Publisher Dharmesh Mistry
Operations Director Robin Ryan
Advertising Director Katie Wood
MD of Advertising Julian Lloyd-Evans
Newstrade Director David Barker
Commercial and Retail Director Martin Belson
Chief Operating Officer Brett Reynolds
Group Finance Director Ian Leggett
Chief Executive James Tye
Chairman Felix Dennis

MAGBOOK

The MagBook brand is a trademark of Dennis
Publishing Ltd. 30 Cleveland St, London W1T 4JD.
Company registered in England. All material ©
Dennis Publishing Ltd, licensed by Felden 2012, and
may not be reproduced in whole or part without the
consent of the publishers. *Eat Yourself Slim* ISBN
1781061211.

LICENSING & SYNDICATION
To license this product, please contact Carlotta
Serantoni on +44 (0) 20 7907 6550 or email
carlotta_serantoni@dennis.co.uk
To syndicate content from this product, please
contact Anj Dosaj Halai on +44 (0) 20 7907 6132
or email anj_dosaj-halai@dennis.co.uk

LIABILITY
While every care was taken during the production
of this MagBook, the publishers cannot be held
responsible for the accuracy of the information
or any consequence arising from it. Dennis
Publishing takes no responsibility for the companies
advertising in this MagBook. The paper used within
this MagBook is produced from sustainable fibre,
manufactured by mills with a valid chain of custody.
Printed at BGPrint Ltd.
Always check with your GP before commencing
an exercise programme, especially if you have
been inactive for a long period of time. Those
with a history of high blood pressure or heart
disease should obtain medical clearance before
undertaking any activity.

Welcome to the Women's Fitness Eat Yourself Slim plan

For more training tips, workouts and the latest fitness news, visit our website at womensfitness.co.uk

Slimming down has never been easier, thanks to our eight-week healthy eating plan. Simply by learning about and eating the right foods you can drop a dress size safely and effectively. Our plan includes delicious and nutritious, healthy recipes for every meal of the day that you can mix and match for eight whole weeks. Plus snacks to keep your metabolism roaring and treats to keep you sweet.

The real key to slimming down is to make sure you're being active as well as eating well, so use our complementary eight-week cardio plan (page 121) to boost your fitness and help you slim down. With options for beginners, intermediates and advanced you'll see results in record time and its progressive nature means you'll never plateau, either. Combine that with our trouble spots workout on page 125, and you'll be looking and feeling fabulous in no time.

So, all you need to do is choose what you fancy from over 130 recipes, plan your weekly meals and get started. Happy slimming!

Joanna Joanna Knight, Editor

contents

the right balance

knowing your food groups is the first step to a healthier, slimmer new you

When it comes to weight loss or weight maintenance, our bodies are actually quite straightforward machines: we simply have to use up more calories than we consume. And the only way to achieve this successfully over the long term is by adopting a healthy lifestyle. Losing weight through diet alone is not always a realistic option, as you may feel like you are starving or depriving yourself of food; but it also doesn't have to mean that you need to run a half marathon three times a week! Invest the time now in improving your lifestyle, and long term you'll see a slimmer, healthier and more energetic you.

The main purpose for food is to give us energy, of which around 60 per cent is used by our vital organs – the brain, heart, liver, kidneys etc – with the rest then used by our body physically. The components of foods have different roles and functions, but they are all designed to work together; therefore, 'diets' that recommend reducing or eliminating certain food groups can damage your health.

fat: the healthy all-rounder

Fat does not necessarily make you fat, as long as you're eating the right fats, and as with all things, in moderation. It's only when we exceed our body's need for fat, or consume the wrong type, that we cause problems such as high blood pressure and obesity. Everybody needs fat in their diet as it plays a role in important functions such as protecting our major organs, including our heart and brain, maintaining body heat and providing key nutrients such as vitamins A, D and E. It is also one of our main sources of energy.

Fats can roughly be grouped into two forms: saturated and unsaturated. We've long thought that saturated fats are unhealthy, but there is now evidence that some may in fact be good for us, and that changing which sat fats we eat can reduce the risk of heart disease. Research shows that sat fats from dairy – milk, cheese and butter – have protective effects against heart disease compared to those found in meat and poultry. Unsaturated fats are purer and contain that all-important omega 3, which is vital for many functions including memory, glowing skin and healthy joints. They can be found in veggie sources such as olive and rapeseed oil, as well as nuts, seeds and fish, especially oily ones like sardines.

carbs: the energy givers

Generally, carbohydrates come from plant foods such as fruits, vegetables, grains and legumes. A key source of energy, they also play a role in the function of our internal organs, our nervous system, and in fuelling our muscles. When eaten, carbohydrates are broken down by the body into simple sugars (called glycogen), which are then used as an energy source.

Like fats, there are essentially two types of carbohydrates – starches and sugars – which can both be found in pure or refined forms:

- Natural sugars – from fruits and vegetables.
- Refined sugars – found in honey, brown sugar, soft drinks, cakes, biscuits, jams and sweets.
- Natural starches – found in wholegrain and wholemeal breakfast cereals, wholemeal flour and bread, wholemeal pasta, brown rice, nuts, potatoes, lentils, chickpeas, bananas and root vegetables like carrots.
- Refined starches – are found in sugary, processed breakfast cereals, white flour, white rice, white pasta, white bread, biscuits and cakes.

Refined carbohydrates are essentially 'white' and have already been broken down into simple sugars, a process your body would normally do. When they are eaten they dump sugar into your bloodstream, resulting in short bursts of energy and mood swings. Sticking to the natural sources will provide more stability in your blood sugars and is much better for you, because they also contain fibre, essential for a healthy gut.

'Invest the time now in improving your lifestyle, and long term you'll be slimmer, healthier and full of energy'

protein: the immunity and body booster

Protein is a key component of our hair, nails, eyes, skin and internal organs and is also essential for a healthy immune system. It allows the body to grow and repair muscles and tissues, while keeping our hormones in check. Good sources of protein include animal meats (skin and fat removed), fish, eggs, milk, yoghurt, nuts, seeds, tofu, beans and oats. Bad sources are essentially those that have been processed such as ham, salami and pies.

fibre: the tummy filler

While not a major food group as such, fibre is important for weight loss as it fills you up and keeps you full for longer. There are two types of fibre – soluble and insoluble. Soluble fibre is found in pulses, fruit and vegetables and helps to reduce the body's 'bad' cholesterol and control blood sugar levels. Insoluble fibre is found in wholewheat bread, brown rice and fruit and helps the passing of food through your intestines, helping to prevent constipation and other gut problems.

how to eat yourself slim

Our bodies are designed to need all food groups for optimal vitality and wellness. Omitting certain food groups can actually cause you to put on weight, as the body goes into survival mode, thinking it is being starved, so it stores fat in order to keep your vital organs functioning and essentially keep you alive. When we start to eat normally again we are adding more calories but not burning off the fat that has been stored, leading to an ever-increasing waistline and a harder battle to shift it. The good news is, *Women's Fitness* has done the hard work for you and developed nutritious and filling recipes to help you lose weight without ever skipping meals. By combining this with the eight-week exercise plan (page 121) and toning exercises (page 125) you'll slim down safely and effortlessly.

When choosing your meals, follow these guidelines to ensure optimum weight loss:

- Your daily fat intake should not exceed 60g, try to keep your saturated fat intake to a minimum.
- Any snacks (an average of one or two a day) should be within your daily calorie allowance.
- There are some delicious sweet treats (page 117) but limit these to a few times a week for best results.

Approximate daily calorie intake required to lose 1-2lbs a week, based on current weight and combined with mild activity:

9st-10st = 1,500-1,700 calories
10st-11st = 1,700-1,900 calories
11st-12st = 1,900-2,000 calories
12st-13st = 2,000-2,200 calories
13st-14st = 2,200-2,400 calories
14st-15st = 2,400-2,500 calories

All you have to do now is pick the recipes you fancy, make a bit of time for exercise and get started. You'll have a body you love for life in no time!

ZAGGORA

SveltMelt
REFRESHING BODY CONTOURING GEL

84%

OF WOMEN
AGREED THAT THE PRODUCT WAS EFFECTIVE
AT SMOOTHING
THE SKIN
AFTER 4 WEEKS

MotionLotion
HYDRATING BODY SCULPTING LOTION

92%

OF WOMEN
AGREED THAT THE PRODUCT WAS EFFECTIVE
AT HYDRATING
AND SMOOTHING THE SKIN
AFTER 4 WEEKS

Consumer User Trial conducted by an independent testing house
with 49 respondents over a 4 week period.

slim down the easy way!

follow these tricks and tips to shape up fast

Now you know the importance of your food groups, the following shortcuts will help to whip you into shape…

kick-start your metabolism

To help your weight loss, you may need to give your metabolism a bit of a boost as it could be a bit sluggish. Breakfast isn't called the most important meal of the day for nothing! Your body has been 'starving' overnight and eating in the morning kick-starts your metabolism, whereas skipping breakfast can actually cause you to gain weight. In fact, do not skip any meals: eat little and often to keep your metabolism ticking over and your blood sugar levels balanced.

Exercise will also help kick-start your metabolism, even if it's a brisk 20-minute walk, because you will continue to burn calories at a faster rate post-workout as your body replenishes and repairs. Protein also plays an important role in your metabolism as your body takes up to 20 per cent more energy to digest it than fats or carbohydrates.

Try to eat your meals within an hour of exercising, too – that way, your body uses the food as energy to repair and replenish rather than storing it as fat.

look for low GI

'GI' stands for Glycaemic Index – the speed at which sugars are broken down and enter your blood stream. High-GI foods (such as refined sugars and starches) are broken down rapidly, whereas low-GI foods provide the slow-release energy that is favoured by our bodies. Low-GI foods include natural carbohydrates, lean proteins and good fats.

control your portions

Portion control is an important part of successful weight loss or maintenance, as it helps you avoid overeating and consuming more calories than you burn off. The following is to be used as a guide to help you stay in control, wherever you are eating:

aim for the following daily intake:

Vegetables	4-5 servings per day (minimum)
Fruit	2 servings per day
Protein	2 servings per day
Nuts and seeds	1 serving per day
Healthy oils	2-3 servings per day
Dairy & alternatives	1 serving per day
Carbs (grains and legumes)	2 servings per day

VEGETABLES AND FRUIT
1 portion = 80g, which is about what you can hold in the palm of one hand.

PROTEIN
1 portion = 70g, the size of a deck of cards.

NUTS AND SEEDS
1 portion = 2tbsp (25g), or a small handful.

HEALTHY OILS
1 portion = 1tbsp.

DAIRY & ALTERNATIVES
1 portion = 180g/180ml.

CARBOHYDRATES
1 portion = size of your clenched fist.

or visualise it on a plate...

- ⅓ made up of vegetables and/or fruit
- About ¼ for grains, potatoes, wholemeal pasta
- About ¼ for protein, such as chicken or fish
- Oils should then be no more than 2tbsp
  (This is an approximate guide)

'Your body has been "starving" overnight, so eating in the morning kick-starts your metabolism, whereas skipping breakfast can cause weight gain'

water: the elixir of life

Water makes up 60 per cent of our body weight and staying hydrated is key when trying to lose weight. Not only does it help your cells to function effectively and flush out toxins, but it also ensures that your metabolism is kept in check. Dehydration can reduce your metabolic rate by 2-3 per cent, making weight loss that bit harder.

Dehydration can also lead to tiredness, constipation, irritability and poor skin, because daily toxins are not being flushed out. This can make you feel demotivated and less likely to feel like sticking to your weight-loss plan in the long term.

Water also helps control your appetite, so you should aim to drink a minimum of 1.5 litres of water a day, and more if you are exercising. The good news, though, is that it doesn't always have to come from plain still water. Create variety with herbal teas, or by adding a slice of lemon, lime or ginger, and eat fruits and vegetables that have a high water content, such as cucumbers, tomatoes, avocados, oranges and melon. These types of fruit and vegetables help to control your blood sugar levels because the body converts them more slowly, and so they provide a more sustained release of energy throughout the day. Avoid alcohol and drinks containing caffeine, sugar or artificial sweeteners, as these contribute to dehydration within the body.

food glossary

get the lowdown on the key
nutrients to include in your diet

Variety is the key to healthy eating and weight loss. Keeping your
foods varied will make sure you don't get bored of eating the
same things – so why not try some new foods each week? It's also
important to maintain a healthy balance by including foods from
each of the different food groups: protein, fats and carbohydrates.
Adding in some wholesome grains, healthy fats and some
delicious herbs and spices will all help you lose weight as they
will control your appetite, balance your blood sugars and can
help to speed up your metabolism, which allows you to burn
calories more efficiently.

grains

OATS are a great, low-GI source of energy. They also contain fibre
and key vitamins and minerals that help maintain blood sugar levels
and can lower cholesterol.

QUINOA not only has the highest protein content of all grains, it has
more calcium than milk, as well as key minerals, iron and B vitamins, all
helping you feel fuller for longer.

RYE is high in antioxidants, which can help to protect the body from
cancer and heart disease, and is also good for balancing blood sugars
and maintaining satiety.

WHOLEWHEAT is always best, as it contains key minerals such as
magnesium, has a low GI, and a high fibre content – which together
are beneficial for weight loss.

BROWN RICE is concentrated in B vitamins and minerals and contains
bran and fibre, which is good news for your digestive system.

SPELT is great for those who may struggle to digest wholewheat and is
high in protein and fibre.

BUCKWHEAT is also good if you are sensitive to gluten. It contains fibre
and protein, as well as magnesium, which helps the muscles to relax.
making it a great post-exercise food.

proteins

EGGS are one of the most complete foods that you can eat. They are packed full of key nutrients including choline, which helps to metabolise fats and is converted by the body to acetylcholine – a molecule that can help to boost your memory.

LEAN WHITE MEATS, namely turkey and chicken, contain an abundance of minerals and vitamins including B vitamins. They are great post-exercise to help with muscle repair.

TOFU is made from soya beans and is high in protein, low in saturated fats and a good source of calcium and vitamin E. A great protein source especially if you are vegetarian.

LEAN RED MEATS, such as beef and lamb, are a great source of iron and B vitamins, both of which are needed for energy.

LEGUMES (BEANS, PEAS AND LENTILS) are high in fibre and excellent for vegetarians. They're packed with vitamins and minerals and help to control blood sugar levels.

DAIRY is high in calcium, which is important for your heart and bones, and is involved in the body's metabolism so can help with weight loss.

FISH is an excellent source of protein as well as essential fats and sulphur, which is required for healthy detoxification.

oils

OLIVE OIL is a monounsaturated fat that's less susceptible to damage when heated and can help reduce cholesterol.

Other oils that can be used include rapeseed, sunflower and safflower, but they should only be used cold in dressings as heating them can change their chemical structure and make them potentially harmful to the body. Make your own salad dressings using olive oil with herbs and spices such as garlic, chilli or rosemary – delicious and with super health benefits.

spices

GINGER is great for cleansing the body and calming the stomach. It also warms the body and boosts circulation.

GARLIC is a fantastic all-rounder. Great for the heart, it also helps to detoxify the liver and lymph system and builds the immune system, so it's a good food to eat for weight loss.

BLACK PEPPER helps to protect against coughs and colds, and helps the body to eliminate toxins.

CHILLIES contain capsaicin, which can lower blood sugars, relax the body and increase metabolism.

MUSTARD strengthens digestion and increases the body's metabolism.

herbs

THYME is great for relaxing muscles, is a good cleanser and contains antiseptic properties, too.

BASIL is antibacterial, mood-enhancing and good for cleansing, and is a source of vitamin C and beta-carotene (a form of vitamin A).

CHIVES can reduce cholesterol and high blood pressure. They are antibacterial and antifungal, too.

CORIANDER is a cleansing herb but is also effective against indigestion.

MINT is good for all things digestion. Use either within foods or add to water (hot or cold) for a refreshing post-meal drink.

PARSLEY is a cleansing and mood-enhancing herb that can have a strong anti-inflammatory effect as well.

ROSEMARY has many health benefits as it is energising, cleansing, stimulating and has antibacterial properties.

TARRAGON can help you sleep and calm your nerves, as well as improve your appetite and digestion.

oatmeal porridge with
walnuts and maple syrup

breakfast

oatmeal porridge with walnuts and maple syrup

Prep and cook time: 20 mins | Soaking: 12 hours | Difficulty: easy

Ingredients (for 4 servings)
200g | 2 cups coarse oatmeal
750ml | 3 cups water
¼tsp salt
50ml | 3½tbsp semi-skimmed milk
50g | ½ cup walnuts, coarsely chopped
2tbsp maple syrup
½tbsp coarse oatmeal

Method
1 Put oatmeal into a large bowl and mix in water. Soak overnight.
2 Put the oatmeal into a pan with the salt. Bring to a boil then simmer gently for 15 minutes, stirring frequently. Add a little more water if the porridge is too thick.
3 Divide between 4 bowls and pour over a little milk. Scatter with the walnuts and drizzle with the maple syrup.

Per serving: Cals 312 Fat 12g Sat fat 0.6g Protein 7.5g

greek yoghurt with figs, nuts, dates and bananas

Prep and cook time: 10 mins | Difficulty: easy

Ingredients (for 4 servings)
1kg | 4 cups low-fat Greek yoghurt
2 figs, halved
1 banana
50g | ½ cup mixed nuts: pecans, hazelnuts, almonds
12 dates
2tbsp honey

Method
1 Divide the yoghurt between 4 bowls, then add the figs, sliced banana and nuts and drizzle with the honey.

Per serving: Cals 348 Fat 7.5g Sat fat 1g Protein 11.2g

strawberry and vanilla protein drink

Prep and cook time: 5 mins | Difficulty: easy

Ingredients (for 4 servings)
Whey protein powder
400g | 2 cups strawberries
1tsp vanilla extract
Honey to taste

Method
1 Make up the protein powder according to the packet instructions to make up a volume of 1L.
2 Whizz the liquid in a blender with the strawberries and vanilla extract and add honey to taste.
3 Serve over ice with strawberries to garnish.

Per serving: Cals 211 Fat 2.4g Sat fat 1g Protein 15.7g

orange and buckthorn smoothie

Prep and cook time: 5 mins | Difficulty: easy

Ingredients (for 4 servings)
250ml | 1 cup sea buckthorn purée
250ml | 1 cup orange juice
500ml | 2 cups buttermilk

To garnish:
Orange zest
Mint leaves

Method
1 Put the buckthorn purée, orange juice and buttermilk together in a blender.
2 Whizz together to combine and pour into 4 glasses.
3 Top with the orange zest and mint to serve.

Per serving: Cals 159 Fat 2.5g Sat fat 1.5g Protein 5.5g

greek yoghurt with figs, dates, nuts and bananas

yoghurt with amaranth, raspberries and raisins

Prep and cook time: 50 mins | Difficulty: easy

Ingredients (for 4 servings)
200g | 2 cups amaranth grains
250g | 2 cups raspberries
75g | ½ cup raisins
50ml | 10tsp apple juice
800ml | 3½ cups low-fat yoghurt
2tsp poppy seeds
12 raspberries, to garnish

Method
1 Put the amaranth in a pan with 500ml water and bring to a boil. Cook for 20 minutes then remove from the heat and cover.
2 Mash the raspberries and set aside for 5 minutes.
3 Put the raisins in a small bowl, pour over the apple juice and let soak.
4 Push the raspberry mixture through a sieve to remove the pips.
5 Fluff the amaranth with a fork and quickly stir through the yoghurt.
6 Divide the yoghurt between 4 bowls and pour over a little of the raspberry purée. Scatter with the raisins and poppy seeds and garnish with the whole raspberries.

Per serving: Cals **290** Fat **5.9g** Sat fat **2.5g** Protein **15g**

avocado spread

Prep and cook time: 10 mins | Difficulty: easy

Ingredients (for 4 servings)
300g | 1¼ cups low-fat cream cheese
3 ripe avocados
Juice of 1 lime
Chives, to garnish
8 slices rye bread, toasted

Method
1 Peel the avocados, remove the stone and mash the flesh.
2 Beat the cream cheese with the lime juice and mashed avocados and season with salt and white pepper.
3 Serve on 2 slices of rye bread, garnish with chopped chives.

Per serving: Cals **383** Fat **15.2g** Sat fat **5g** Protein **8.5g**

banana and oat muffins

Prep and cook time: 50 mins | Difficulty: easy

Ingredients (for 12 muffins)
100g | 1 cup porridge oats
125g | 1¼ cups plain flour
1tsp baking powder
½tsp bicarbonate of soda
½tsp ground cinnamon
½tsp salt
100g | ½ cup butter
200g | 1 cup sugar
2 medium eggs, beaten
2 bananas, mashed

Method
1 Heat the oven to 180ºC/375ºF/Gas Mark 5.
2 Cut a sheet of kitchen parchment into 12 squares of 15 cm/6in x 15cm/6in and line a muffin tray.
3 Put the oats, flour, baking powder, bicarbonate of soda, cinnamon and salt into a bowl and mix.
4 Beat together the butter and sugar and gradually add the eggs.
5 Fold into the flour mixture then stir in the bananas.
6 Divide the mixture between the lined cases and bake for 25-30 minutes.

Per serving: Cals **239** Fat **9.4g** Sat fat **5g** Protein **3.5g**

mango smoothie with frozen raspberries

Prep and cook time: 10 mins | Difficulty: easy

Ingredients (for 4 glasses)
3 large ripe mangoes
500ml | 2 cups semi-skimmed milk
12 frozen raspberries

Method
1 Peel the mangoes and cut the flesh from the stone, reserving any juice.
2 Put the mango flesh and juice in a blender with the milk and whizz until smooth.
3 Thread the raspberries onto 4 cocktail sticks and serve with the smoothies.

Per serving: Cals **165** Fat **3.2g** Sat fat **1.5g** Protein **4.75g**

blueberry pancakes

Prep and cook time: 45 mins | Difficulty: easy

Ingredients (for 6 servings)
200g | 2 cups flour
2tsp baking powder
1 pinch salt
2 eggs, separated
300ml | 1⅓ cups semi-skimmed milk
2tbsp clear honey
200g | 2 cups blueberries

Method
1 Put the flour, baking powder, salt, egg yolks, milk and honey into
  a mixing bowl and beat to make a smooth batter. Let rest for
  30 minutes.
2 Whisk the egg whites until stiff then fold into the batter with half
  the blueberries.
3 Heat a non-stick frying pan, drop in spoonfuls of batter and cook for
  2-3 minutes on one side, then turn and cook the other side. Take out
  of the pan and keep warm. Continue making pancakes in this way
  until all the batter is used up.
4 Pile the pancakes on plates and serve with the rest of the blueberries.

Per serving: Cals **245** Fat **3.8g** Sat fat **1.3g** Protein **8.3g**

muesli with nuts

Prep and cook time: 10 mins | Difficulty: easy

Ingredients (for 1kg)
200g | 2 cups rolled oats
200g | 2 cups wheat flakes
100g | 2 cups maize flakes
100g | ⅔ cup cashew nuts
100g | ⅔ cup Brazil nuts, chopped
100g | ⅔ cup hazelnuts, skinned and unskinned
100g | 2 cups barley flakes
100g | 1 cup corn flakes

Method
Mix the ingredients together and store in an airtight container.
Serve a 45g portion with 125ml semi-skimmed milk (not included in
nutritional values).

Per 45g serving: Cals **194** Fat **17.6g** Sat fat **1.4g** Protein **4.5g**

yoghurt with mandarins, muesli, grapes and seeds

Prep and cook time: 10 mins | Difficulty: easy

Ingredients (for 4 servings)
1kg | 4 cups low-fat yoghurt
2 mandarins, peeled, pith removed and halved
12 black grapes
4tbsp muesli
2tbsp sunflower seeds
Mint leaves, to garnish

Method
1 Put the yoghurt into 4 bowls and top with the mandarins, grapes,
  muesli and sunflower seeds. Garnish with the mint leaves.

Per serving: Cals **273** Fat **7g** Sat fat **3g** Protein **17g**

cheese and tomato on toast

Prep and cook time: 10 mins | Difficulty: easy

Ingredients (for 4 servings)
200g | 2 cups reduced-fat Cheddar cheese, grated
4 tomatoes, sliced
8 slices brown bread

Method
1 Heat the grill to its highest setting.
2 Toast the bread on one side then sprinkle the cheese over each slice,
  top with the tomatoes and grill until the cheese has melted.

Per serving: Cals **262** Fat **6.6g** Sat fat **2.9g** Protein **21.1g**

boiled egg

Prep and cook time: 10 mins | Difficulty: easy

Ingredients (for 4 servings)
4 medium eggs
4 slices rye bread, toasted

Method
1 Bring a pan of salted water to the boil and gently lower in the eggs.
2 Cook for 3-4 minutes for a soft-boiled egg, 5 minutes for medium-
  boiled and 7 minutes for hard-boiled. Serve with the toasted bread.

Per serving: Cals **161** Fat **6g** Sat fat **2g** Protein **9g**

grilled mushrooms, tomato and turkey ham with spinach and poached eggs

porridge with blueberries

Prep and cook time: 5 mins | Difficulty: easy

Ingredients (for 4 servings)
200g | 2 cups porridge oats
1.2L | 5 cups water
200g | 2 cups blueberries

Method
1 Put the oats and water in a saucepan and bring to the boil.
2 Turn the heat down and cook for 5 minutes, stirring all the time.
3 Divide between 4 bowls and serve with blueberries scattered on top.

Per serving: Cals 214 Fat 3g Sat fat 0.5g Protein 5.8g

seville orange marmalade with wholemeal toast

Prep and cook time: 3 hours | Difficulty: medium

Ingredients (for 6 450g/1lb jars)
900g | 2lb Seville oranges
2L | 8 cups water
Juice of 2 lemons
1.8kg | 4lb sugar

To serve:
1 slice wholemeal toast

Method
1 Put the oranges in a large pan with the water, bring to the boil and simmer for 2 hours.
2 Remove the fruit, keeping the water in the pan, and cut in half. Remove the pips from the fruit, set them aside and chop the fruit finely.
3 Put the pips in a separate small pan, cover with water and boil for 5 minutes.
4 Return the chopped fruit to the pan of water, add the lemon juice and the water from the pip pan. Add the sugar and bring to the boil, stirring until the sugar is dissolved.
5 Boil for about 15 minutes or until set. Drop a teaspoon of the mixture onto a chilled saucer, let cool and push it with your fingertip. If the skin wrinkles, the marmalade is done.
6 Remove any scum from the surface, stir well and let sit for 15 minutes. Pour into sterilised jars and screw on the lids.
7 Serve 1 heaped teaspoon of the marmalade with wholemeal toast.

Per serving: Cals 141 Fat 1g Sat fat 0g Protein 4g

grilled mushrooms, tomato and turkey ham with spinach and poached egg

Prep and cook time: 30 mins | Difficulty: medium

Ingredients (for 4 servings)
400g | 1lb spinach, washed and stalks removed
2tbsp low-fat crème fraîche
8 slices turkey ham
Salt and pepper to taste
4 large field mushrooms, stalks removed
2 large tomatoes, halved
4 medium eggs
Chopped parsley, to garnish

Method
1 Put the wet spinach in a large pan and cook until wilted. Drain, squeeze out excess moisture and chop. Mix with the crème fraîche, season with salt and pepper and keep warm.
2 Grill the turkey ham until crisp then set aside and keep warm.
3 Grill the mushrooms and tomato halves until just tender. Keep warm.
4 Fill a wide pan with 8cm/3in water. Bring to the boil then turn the heat down until only a few bubbles rise to the surface.
5 Break the eggs into individual cups and carefully slip into the water. Poach for about 3 minutes then remove with a slotted spoon.
6 Arrange the tomatoes, turkey ham and mushrooms on a plate, top with the spinach and poached egg and season with salt and pepper.

Per serving: Cals 175 Fat 9.6g Sat fat 2.5g Protein 15.7g

blueberry smoothie

Prep and cook time: 5 mins | Difficulty: easy

Ingredients (for 4 servings)
200g | 2 cups blueberries
2 bananas
500ml | 2 cups low-fat yoghurt

Method
1 Put the blueberries, bananas and yoghurt into a blender and whizz until smooth.
2 Pour into 4 glasses and serve.

Per serving: Cals 142 Fat 2g Sat fat 0.5g Protein 7.2g

pancakes with raspberry coulis

Prep and cook time: 45 mins | Difficulty: easy

Ingredients (for 6 servings)
For the pancakes:
200g | 2 cups flour
2tsp baking powder
1 pinch salt
2 medium eggs, separated
300ml | 1⅓ cups semi-skimmed milk
2tbsp clear honey

For the coulis:
400g | 3 cups raspberries
50g | ¼ cup caster sugar

Method

1 Put the flour, baking powder, salt, egg yolks, milk and honey into a mixing bowl and beat to make a smooth batter. Let rest for 30 minutes.
2 Meanwhile place the raspberries and sugar in a pan and cook on a medium heat for 4-5 minutes, stirring until the fruit collapses. Place a fine sieve over a bowl and pass the fruit through to deseed. Cool for 10 minutes, then keep in the fridge until needed.
3 Whisk the egg whites until stiff then fold into the batter.
4 Heat a non-stick frying pan, drop in spoonfuls of batter and cook for 2-3 minutes on one side, then turn and cook the other side. Take out of the pan and keep warm. Continue making pancakes in this way until all the batter is used up.
5 Serve the pancakes with the coulis drizzled over the top.

Per serving: Cals **288** Fat **3.5g** Sat fat **1.3g** Protein **3.5g**

strawberry and almond smoothie

Prep and cook time: 10 mins | Chilling: 30 mins | Difficulty: easy

Ingredients (for 4 servings)
400g | 2 cups strawberries
2tbsp ground almonds
1tbsp almond syrup
1tbsp strawberry syrup, optional
300ml | 1⅓ cups low-fat yogurt

To garnish:
Flaked almonds, strawberry slices

Method

1 Lay the strawberries in a shallow dish and place in the freezer for 30 minutes to freeze slightly.
2 Put the strawberries, ground almonds, both syrups and the yoghurt in a blender and whizz until smooth.
3 Divide between 4 glasses and garnish with flaked almonds and strawberry slices.

Per serving: Cals **143** Fat **6.3g** Sat fat **1.1g** Protein **6.2g**

orange smoothie with oatmeal

Prep and cook time 10 mins | Difficulty: easy

Ingredients (for 4 glasses)
2 bananas
4 oranges
2tsp honey
4tbsp oatmeal
250g | 1 cup low-fat yoghurt
400ml | 1⅔ cups buttermilk

To garnish
4tsp oatmeal
Mint leaves

Method

1 Peel the bananas and place in a blender.
2 Squeeze the juice from the oranges and add to the bananas with the honey, oatmeal, yoghurt and buttermilk.
3 Whizz until smooth and serve in 4 glasses with the oatmeal and mint leaves to garnish.

Per serving: Cals **295** Fat **4.3g** Sat fat **2g** Protein **11.3g**

couscous porridge with pears

Prep and cook time: 15 mins | Difficulty: easy

Ingredients (for 4 servings)
400ml | 1⅔ cups apple juice, heated
400g | 2⅓ cups instant couscous
3 pears, peeled, cores removed and roughly chopped
2tbsp honey
Juice of 1 lemon
1 pinch cinnamon
Mint leaves, to garnish

Method

1 Pour the hot apple juice over the couscous and let the couscous absorb the juice for 5 minutes, stirring occasionally.
2 Place the pears in a saucepan with the honey, lemon juice and cinnamon and bring to a boil.
3 Remove from the heat and mix in with the couscous.
4 Serve in bowls garnished with mint leaves.

Per serving: Cals **273** Fat **1.9g** Sat fat **0g** Protein **4.25g**

pear yoghurt shake with cinnamon

Prep and cook time: 15 mins | Difficulty: easy

Ingredients (for 4 servings)
2 ripe pears, peeled, quartered, cored and chopped
800ml | 3½ cups low-fat yoghurt
2tbsp honey
½tsp ground cinnamon
1 pinch nutmeg

To garnish:
Ground cinnamon

Method

1 Put the pears, yoghurt, honey, cinnamon and nutmeg into a blender and whizz until smooth.
2 Pour into glasses and sprinkle with a little cinnamon to serve.

Per serving: Cals **207** Fat **4g** Sat fat **2g** Protein **12.5g**

poached egg with spinach on toast

Prep and cook time: 15 mins | Difficulty: easy

Ingredients (for 4 servings)
800g | 2lb spinach, washed and stalks removed
4 medium eggs
4 slices brown bread, toasted

Method

1 Put the wet spinach in a large pan with a lid and cook for 2 minutes or until wilted. Drain in a colander, squeeze out excess liquid and chop roughly. Keep warm.
2 Put cold water to a depth of about 8cm/3in in a wide pan. Bring to the boil then turn the heat down until only a few bubbles rise to the surface.
3 Break the eggs into individual cups and carefully slip into the water. Poach for about 3 minutes then remove with a slotted spoon.
4 Put the spinach on the toast, top each with an egg and serve.

Per serving: Cals **182** Fat **6g** Sat fat **2g** Protein **14g**

raspberry, banana and pink grapefruit smoothie

Prep and cook time: 5 mins | Difficulty: easy

Ingredients (for 4 glasses)
3 bananas, sliced
250g | 2 cups raspberries
1tbsp honey
600ml | 2½ cups pink grapefruit juice
8 raspberries, to garnish

Method

1 Put the bananas, raspberries, honey and grapefruit juice into a blender.
2 Whizz together until the fruits are blended and smooth.
3 Pour into 4 glasses and serve topped with a couple of raspberries on each.

Per serving: Cals **173** Fat **0.5g** Sat fat **0g** Protein **1.8g**

yoghurt with berries, amaranth and sunflower seeds

melon and oat drink

Prep and cook time: 10 mins | Difficulty: easy

Ingredients (for 4 servings)
1 Galia melon, peeled and seeds removed
1L | 4 cups oat milk
12 basil leaves
Honey to taste

Method
1 Put the melon flesh in a blender with the oat milk and 4 basil leaves. Blend until smooth, add honey to taste and pour into glasses. Garnish with the reserved basil leaves.

Per serving: Cals **150** Fat **2.5g** Sat fat **0g** Protein **3.2g**

blackcurrant smoothie

Prep and cook time: 5 mins | Difficulty: easy

Ingredients (for 4 servings)
400g | 1lb blackcurrants
2 bananas
1L | 4 cups low-fat yoghurt
2tbsp honey
4 ice cubes

Method
1 Put all the ingredients in a blender and whizz until smooth.

Per serving: Cals **264** Fat **5g** Sat fat **2.5g** Protein **9g**

muesli with bananas, grapes and passion fruit

Prep and cook time: 2 hours 10 mins | Difficulty: easy

Ingredients (for 4 servings)
200g | 2½ cups rolled oats
500ml | 2 cups semi-skimmed milk
3 bananas
200g | 2 cups grapes
4 passion fruit

Method
1 Soak the oats in the milk for 2 hours.
2 Divide the oats between 4 bowls and serve with the sliced bananas, grapes and passion fruit flesh on top.

Per serving: Cals **370** Fat **5.5g** Sat fat **2g** Protein **10.7g**

yoghurt with berries, amaranth and sunflower seeds

Prep and cook time: 50 mins | Difficulty: easy

Ingredients (for 4 servings)
200g | ¾ cup amaranth grains
1L | 4 cups low-fat yoghurt
100g | 1 cup strawberries, halved
125g | 1 cup raspberries
100g | 1 cup redcurrants
100g | 1 cup blueberries
2tbsp sunflower seeds

Method
1 Put the amaranth grains in a pan with 500ml water and bring to a boil.
2 Boil for 20 minutes, then remove from the heat and cover. Let sit for 15 minutes then fluff up the grains with a fork.
3 Stir the amaranth through the yoghurt, reserving some to garnish.
4 Put the yoghurt into 4 bowls and scatter over the berries, sunflower seeds and remaining amaranth.

Per serving: Cals **272** Fat **7.1g** Sat fat **3g** Protein **19.4g**

carrot, courgette and pineapple juice

Prep and cook time: 10 mins | Difficulty: easy

Ingredients (for 4 servings)
1 pineapple, peeled
2 carrots, washed
1 courgette, washed

Method
1 Quarter the pineapple and cut away the central woody core. Cut into long thin wedges.
2 Trim the end off the carrots and courgette.
3 Press the pineapple, carrots and courgette through a juicer and mix well before serving.

Per serving: Cals **73** Fat **0.3g** Sat fat **0g** Protein **1.7g**

spirulina, cucumber and avocado smoothie

Prep and cook time: 5 mins | Difficulty: easy

Ingredients (for 4 servings)
1 cucumber, chopped
2 ripe avocados, quartered
2tsp spirulina powder
Juice of 1 lime
1 spring onion, chopped
2 sprigs fresh coriander
Dash chilli sauce

Method
1 Put the cucumber into a blender.
2 Peel the avocado, remove the flesh from the stone and add to the blender with the spirulina powder, lime juice, spring onion, coriander and chilli sauce.
3 Add 500ml cold water and blend everything together. Pour into glasses and serve.

Per serving: Cals **152** Fat **14.2g** Sat fat **2g** Protein **3.5g**

oatmeal porridge with dates and bananas

Prep and cook time: 20 mins | Soaking: 12 hours | Difficulty: easy

Ingredients (for 4 servings)
200g | 2 cups fine or medium oatmeal
750ml | 3 cups water
75ml | 2/3 cup semi-skimmed milk
6 dates, chopped
2 bananas, sliced
4tsp ground linseeds

Method
1 Put the oatmeal in a bowl, mix in the water and soak overnight.
2 Put the oatmeal and milk into a pan, bring to the boil then simmer gently for about 15 minutes. Add a little more milk if necessary.
3 Serve the porridge with the dates, bananas and ground linseeds scattered over.

Per serving: Cals **304** Fat **3.8g** Sat fat **1g** Protein **7.33g**

crunchy muesli with berries and honey

Prep and cook time: 15 mins | Difficulty: easy

Ingredients (for 4 servings)
1kg | 4 cups low-fat yoghurt
1 apple
125g | 1 cup raspberries
125g | 1 cup blackberries
4tbsp crunchy muesli
4tsp honey
Mint leaves, to garnish

Method
1 Divide the yoghurt between 4 bowls. Peel, quarter and core the apple and cut into small slices. Place the apple into the bowls and mix with the yoghurt.
2 Wash the berries and carefully pat dry. Spoon some of the crunchy muesli and a few berries over the yoghurt and drizzle some honey on top. Garnish with mint leaves and serve.

Per serving: Cals **392** Fat **6.5g** Sat fat **2.5g** Protein **18.2g**

soya smoothie with melon

Prep and cook time: 5 mins | **Difficulty:** easy

Ingredients (for 4 servings)
3 bananas
750ml | 3 cups soya milk
1tbsp honey

To garnish:
½ cantaloupe melon
Mint leaves
4 stalks rosemary

Method
1 Put the bananas and soya milk into a blender and blend until smooth.
2 Remove all but the top leaves from the rosemary stalks. Scoop balls from the melon and thread them onto the rosemary stalks.
3 Serve the smoothie with the melon skewers and mint to garnish.

Per serving: Cals **144** Fat **2.1g** Sat fat **0g** Protein **5.5g**

banana bread

Prep and cook time: 1 hour 10 mins | **Difficulty:** easy

Ingredients (for 1 loaf)
150g | ¾ cup soft brown sugar
50g | ¼ cup butter, melted
2 medium eggs
1tsp vanilla essence
4tbsp water
3 ripe bananas, mashed
200g | 2 cups plain flour
1tsp salt
1tsp ground cinnamon
1tsp baking powder
1tsp bicarbonate of soda

Method
1 Preheat the oven to 180ºC/375ºF/Gas Mark 5.
2 In a medium bowl, beat the sugar and butter until smooth and creamy. Beat in the eggs, vanilla essence, water and bananas with the sugar mixture until well blended.
3 Mix in the flour, cinnamon, bicarbonate of soda, salt and baking powder. Pour into a greased 1kg/2lb loaf tin and bake for 45-60 minutes. It is done when the top is firm and it is a golden brown colour. Let cool on a wire rack. Slice into 12 and serve.

Per serving: Cals **201** Fat **6.7g** Sat fat **2.8g** Protein **3.9g**

rye bread with peanut butter and bananas

Prep and cook time: 25 mins | **Difficulty:** easy

Ingredients (for 4 servings)
400g |1lb shelled peanuts
Approx 2tbsp groundnut oil
4 slices rye bread
2 bananas, sliced

Method
1 Heat the oven to 150ºC/300ºF/Gas Mark 2.
2 Put the peanuts on a baking tray and roast in the oven for about 15 minutes.
3 Put the peanuts in a blender with the oil and whizz until you have the required consistency. Season with salt to taste.
4 Spread each slice of bread with 1 tablespoon of peanut butter and top with banana slices.

Per serving: Cals **187** Fat **6.3g** Sat fat **0.8g** Protein **5.8g**

carrot muffins

Prep and cook time: 45 mins | **Difficulty:** easy

Ingredients (for 12 muffins)
180g | 1¾ cups plain flour, sifted
100g | ½ cup soft brown sugar
½tsp ground cinnamon
½tsp salt
2tsp baking powder
1 pinch baking soda
50ml | 10tsp semi-skimmed milk
2 medium eggs
60g | ¼ cup butter, melted
1 banana, mashed
150g | 3 cups carrots, grated

Method
1 Heat the oven to 200ºC/400ºF/Gas Mark 6. Line a muffin tray with 12 paper muffin cases.
2 Put the flour into a bowl with the sugar, cinnamon, salt, baking powder and baking soda.
3 In a separate bowl, whisk the milk with the eggs and butter and add to the flour mixture.
4 Add the banana and carrots and mix well. Divide the mixture between the muffin cases and bake for about 25 minutes.

Per serving: Cals **171** Fat **5.8g** Sat fat **3.2g** Protein **3.4g**

muesli with dried fruit

kedgeree

Prep and cook time: 35 mins | Difficulty: easy

Ingredients (for 4 servings)
1tbsp olive oil
1 onion, finely chopped
1tsp garam masala
300g | 1½ cups long-grain rice
600ml | 2½ cups fish stock
1 spring onion, finely chopped
300g | 12oz smoked haddock, roughly flaked
Salt and pepper, to taste
3 hard-boiled medium eggs, chopped
4tbsp chopped parsley
Juice of 1 lemon

Method

1 Heat the oil in a wide pan and gently cook the onion and garam masala.
2 Add the rice and cook for a further minute, stirring. Add the stock, bring to the boil and simmer, covered, for about 20 minutes until the rice has absorbed the liquid. Add a little water if necessary.
3 Add the spring onion and fish 5 minutes before serving and season.
4 Before serving, stir in the chopped egg, parsley and lemon and warm over a medium heat for 2 minutes.

Per serving: Cals **308** Fat **9.5g** Sat fat **2g** Protein **30g**

muesli with dried fruit

Prep and cook time: 10 mins | Difficulty: easy

Ingredients (for 1kg)
200g | 2 cups wheat flakes
200g | 2 cups rolled oats
100g | 1 cup barley flakes
100g | 1½ cups puffed rice
100g | ⅔ cup dried goji berries
50g | ⅓ cup raisins
50g | ⅓ cup dried cranberries
50g | ⅓ cup pumpkin seeds
50g | ⅓ cup dried apricots, chopped
50g | ⅔ cup dried coconut
50g | ⅓ cup, dates chopped
250ml | 1 cup low-fat yoghurt

Method

1 Combine all the dry ingredients and store in an airtight container.
2 Serve 40g of muesli with yoghurt.

Per 40g serving: Cals **363** Fat **9.3g** Sat fat **5.3g** Protein **19g**

bran flakes with blueberries

Prep and cook time: 2 mins | Difficulty: easy

Ingredients (for 4 servings)
180g | 4 cups bran flakes
200g | 2 cups blueberries
500ml | 2 cups semi-skimmed milk

Method

1 Divide the bran flakes and blueberries between 4 bowls and serve with the milk.

Per 45g serving: Cals **201** Fat **3.5g** Sat fat **1.5g** Protein **8.2g**

grilled halloumi and mushrooms with paprika and cream cheese

Prep and cook time: 30 mins | Difficulty: easy

Ingredients (for 4 servings)
2tbsp low-fat cream cheese
1 spring onion, finely chopped
1 sprig rosemary, finely chopped
1 sprig thyme, finely chopped
1tsp paprika
Juice of ½ lemon
Salt and pepper to taste
1tbsp olive oil
4 large field mushrooms, stalks removed
4 slices rye bread
200g | 8oz halloumi, sliced
Thyme, to garnish

Method

1 Combine the cream cheese with the spring onions, rosemary, thyme, paprika and lemon juice. Season with salt and pepper and set aside.
2 Heat a griddle pan until it's very hot. Brush the mushrooms, bread and halloumi with a little oil and grill for about 3 minutes on each side.
3 Serve the mushrooms and halloumi on the toast with the paprika cream cheese and garnish with thyme leaves.

Per serving: Cals **293** Fat **22.7g** Sat fat **1.5g** Protein **16.9g**

quinoa with ajvar, asparagus and poached egg

Prep and cook time: 1 hour | Difficulty: easy

Ingredients (for 4 servings)
For the ajvar:
1 large aubergine
3 red peppers
1 clove garlic, chopped
Juice of 1 lemon
1tbsp olive oil
Salt and pepper to taste

For the salad:
200g | 1 cup quinoa
1 bunch asparagus
200g | 8oz mangetout
2 spring onions, sliced diagonally
4 medium eggs

Method
1 Heat the oven to 240°C/475°F/Gas Mark 9.
2 Put the aubergine and peppers on a baking sheet and roast until their skins blacken and blister. Transfer to a large bowl, cover with cling film and let cool for 10 minutes.
3 Peel away and discard the skins, seeds and stems. Purée the flesh with the garlic, lemon juice and oil, season with salt and pepper and set aside.
4 Cook the quinoa according to the packet instructions. Drain, rinse and stir through most of the ajvar, leaving a little to serve on the side.
5 Bring a large pan of salted water to the boil and cook the asparagus and mangetout until just tender. Drain well and stir through the quinoa along with the spring onions.
6 Fill a wide pan with 8cm/3in water. Bring to the boil then turn the heat down until only a few bubbles rise to the surface.
7 Break the eggs into individual cups and carefully slip into the water. Poach for about 3 minutes then remove with a slotted spoon.
8 Serve the eggs on top of the salad with extra ajvar on the side.

Per serving: Cals **326** Fat **11.7g** Sat fat **2.5g** Protein **15.2g**

banana and walnut shake

Prep and cook time: 5 mins | Difficulty: easy

Ingredients (for 4 servings)
4 bananas, sliced
8tbsp low-fat yoghurt
125g | 1 cup walnuts, chopped
2tbsp honey

Method
1 Put the bananas into a blender and add the yoghurt, walnuts and honey.
2 Whizz until thoroughly blended, then pour into glasses and serve.

Per serving: Cals **307** Fat **4.4g** Sat fat **1.5g** Protein **12.8g**

yoghurt with fruit, nuts and rolled oats

Prep and cook time: 5 mins | Difficulty: easy

Ingredients (for 4 servings)
1kg | 4 cups low-fat yoghurt
4 small apples, cored and quartered
2 bananas, sliced
4tbsp rolled oats
4tbsp walnuts, shelled
2tbsp honey
Mint leaves, to garnish

Method
1 Put the yoghurt into 4 bowls, add the fruit, nuts and oats and drizzle over the honey.

Per serving: Cals **404** Fat **9.9g** Sat fat **3.2g** Protein **16.5g**

spinach and potato tortilla

lunch

spinach and potato tortilla

Prep and cook time: 15 mins | Difficulty: easy

Ingredients (for 2 servings)
1tbsp olive oil
100g | 4oz new potatoes, boiled and sliced
3 medium eggs
Salt and pepper to taste
80g | 1 cup baby spinach, washed

Method
1 Heat the oil in a 15 cm/6in non-stick frying pan and sauté the
  potatoes until lightly browned.
2 Whisk the eggs in a cup and season with salt and pepper.
  Pour over the potatoes and scatter with the spinach.
3 Cover with a pan lid and cook over a low-medium heat for about
  4 minutes, or until the egg is set. Slide onto a plate and serve.

Per serving: Cals 191 Fat 13.3g Sat fat 4g Protein 9.8g

chicken salad in pitta bread

Prep and cook time: 15 mins | Difficulty: easy

Ingredients (for 4 servings)
3tbsp reduced-fat mayonnaise
4 spring onions, finely chopped
2 cooked chicken breasts, or leftover roast chicken
4 pitta breads
8 lettuce leaves, torn
Pinch paprika
1tbsp chopped parsley
Salt and pepper to taste

Method
1 Mix the mayonnaise with the spring onions and chicken.
  Season with salt and pepper.
2 Slit open the pitta breads and stuff with the lettuce and
  mayonnaise mixture.
3 Sprinkle with the paprika and chopped parsley.

Per serving: Cals 328 Fat 6g Sat fat 1.8g Protein 27.3g

grilled chicken breast with couscous and mint

Prep and cook time: 20 mins | Marinade: 15 mins | Difficulty: easy

Ingredients (for 2 servings)
For the chicken:
2 chicken breasts
Juice of 1 lemon
1tsp honey
2tsp grain mustard

For the couscous:
150g | 1 cup couscous
300ml | 1⅓ cups chicken stock, boiling
1 red onion, finely chopped
1 garlic clove, finely chopped
1 bunch mint, chopped
½ bunch flat-leaf parsley, chopped
½ cucumber, peeled and diced
1tbsp olive oil
Salt and pepper to taste
Juice of 1 lemon

Method
1 Put the chicken breasts between two sheets of cling film and bash
  with a rolling pin to flatten.
2 Mix together the lemon juice, honey and mustard, rub into the chicken
  breasts and leave to marinate for 15 minutes.
3 Place the couscous into a bowl, add the boiling stock and leave to
  soak for 10 minutes.
4 Fry the onion in a non-stick frying pan until translucent then add
  the garlic and cook for 2 minutes. Let cool slightly and add to
  the couscous.
5 Add the herbs and cucumber and drizzle with oil and lemon juice.
  Mix well and season to taste with salt and pepper.
6 Heat a griddle pan until very hot then cook the chicken for about 3
  minutes each side, turning once to make a criss-cross pattern.
7 Slice the chicken and serve with the couscous.

Per serving: Cals 213 Fat 6.5g Sat fat 1g Protein 20.4g

grilled chicken breast with couscous and mint

steak with roast cherry tomatoes on grilled bread

Prep and cook time: 30 mins | Difficulty: easy

Ingredients (for 4 servings)
6 slices rustic bread
2 cloves garlic, chopped
2tbsp olive oil
400g | 1lb cherry tomatoes, halved
Salt and pepper to taste
2 large rump steaks, trimmed
Thyme sprigs, to garnish

Method
1 Cut the crusts off 2 of the slices of bread and set aside the others.
2 Heat the oven to 200°C/400°F/Gas Mark 6 and put the crust-less bread slices on the bottom shelf in the oven for 5 minutes.
3 Remove the bread from the oven, crumble to make coarse breadcrumbs and mix with the garlic and a tablespoon of oil. Set aside.
4 Place the tomatoes in a baking tin. Sprinkle with a little salt and roast for about 5 minutes or until the skins start to blister. Remove from the oven.
5 Heat the remaining oil in a griddle pan until very hot. Season the meat with a little black pepper and cook for about 3 minutes each side. Remove from the pan and rest for 5 minutes, then slice.
6 Wipe the griddle pan dry, return to the heat and toast the remaining bread on both sides. Keep warm.
7 Top the toasted bread with the tomatoes, sliced steak and garlic breadcrumbs. Garnish with thyme sprigs.

Per serving: Cals **363** Fat **12.1g** Sat fat **1g** Protein **25.1g**

aubergines, tomato and feta cheese salad

Prep and cook time: 30 mins | Difficulty: easy

Ingredients (for 4 servings)
2 large aubergines, chopped into large chunks
Salt and pepper to taste
2 cloves garlic, finely chopped
12 cherry tomatoes
1tbsp balsamic vinegar
2tbsp white wine vinegar
2tbsp olive oil
150g | 1 cup feta cheese, roughly crumbled
Basil leaves, to garnish

Method
1 Heat the oven to 200°C/400°F/Gas Mark 6.
2 In a non-stick pan dry fry the aubergines on all sides for about 10 minutes or until browned and tender.
3 Add the garlic and fry briefly, season with salt and pepper, remove from the heat and let cool slightly.
4 Place the tomatoes in an ovenproof dish. Bake for around 15 minutes in the preheated oven.
5 Whisk together the vinegars and oil, season with salt and pepper and toss with the aubergines.
6 To serve, arrange the aubergine on plates, scatter with feta cheese, top with the tomatoes and garnish with basil.

Per serving: Cals **244** Fat **15.3g** Sat fat **6.5g** Protein **7.4g**

spicy sweet potato soup with ginger

Prep and cook time: 30 mins | Difficulty: easy

Ingredients (For 4 servings)
2 onions, chopped
1 clove garlic, chopped
1 thumb-sized piece fresh ginger, peeled and grated
1 red chilli, deseeded and chopped
2 sweet potatoes, peeled and cubed
2tbsp sherry vinegar
1L | 4 cups vegetable stock
100ml | 7tbsp sour cream
1 pinch cinnamon
Salt and pepper to taste
25g | ¼ cup goats' cheese
Zest of 1 lime

Method
1 Cook the onion in a non-stick frying pan until soft. Add the garlic, ginger and chilli and cook for 2 minutes.
2 Add the sweet potatoes; stir for 2 minutes then add the vinegar and the stock. Cover with a lid and simmer for about 15 minutes until the potatoes are soft.
3 Purée the soup with a hand blender, then stir in the sour cream and gently reheat. Season with salt, pepper and cinnamon.
4 Ladle the soup into bowls, crumble some goats' cheese over the top and garnish with the lime zest.

Per serving: Cals **173** Fat **6.2g** Sat fat **3.9g** Protein **3.2g**

mixed leaves with artichokes, roast peppers and goats' cheese

Prep and cook time: 30 mins | Difficulty: easy

Ingredients (for 4 servings)
4 red peppers, deseeded and halved
6 globe artichokes
2tbsp olive oil
Juice of 1 lemon
2tbsp chopped basil
Salt and pepper to taste
2 bags mixed leaves
100g | 1 cup black olives
100g | 1 cup soft goats' cheese, crumbled

Method
1 Heat the oven to 220ºC/425ºF/Gas Mark 7.
2 Roast the peppers in the oven, skin-side up, for about 15 minutes or until the skins start to blister and burn. Remove from the oven, put in a bowl and cover with cling film.
3 Meanwhile, remove the outer leaves from the artichokes, trim the tops and stalks and cut in half lengthways. Using a sharp spoon, remove the hairy fibres from the middle.
4 Bring a large pan of salted water to the boil and cook the artichokes for about 8 minutes or until tender. Drain well and set aside.
5 Mix the oil with the lemon juice, stir in the basil and season with salt and pepper.
6 Remove the skins from the red peppers and roughly chop the flesh.
7 Arrange the leaves, artichokes, peppers and olives on serving plates, scatter over the goats' cheese and drizzle with the dressing. Serve immediately.

Per serving: Cals **210** Fat **14.7g** Sat fat **4.7g** Protein **13.7g**

chicken kebabs with tabouleh

Prep and cook time: 40 mins | Difficulty: easy

Ingredients (for 4 servings)
100g | 1 cup bulgur wheat
2 chicken breasts, skinned
2tbsp chilli sauce
4 large tomatoes, skinned, seeds removed and finely diced
1 cucumber, peeled and finely diced
2 cloves garlic, crushed
1 bunch parsley, chopped
1tsp mint, chopped
4 spring onions, chopped
Juice of 2 lemons
3tbsp olive oil
Salt and pepper to taste
Lemon wedges, to garnish

Method
1 Put the bulgur wheat in a bowl and pour 1 litre boiling water over it. Mix well, cover and leave for 30 minutes.
2 Meanwhile, cut the chicken into cubes and thread onto wooden skewers. Brush with the chilli sauce.
3 Mix the bulgur wheat with the other ingredients and season.
4 In a non-stick frying pan gently cook the chicken kebabs until browned and cooked through.
5 Serve the kebabs with the tabouleh and lemon wedges.

Per serving: Cals 272 Fat 13.2g Sat fat 2g Protein 18g

miso soup with seaweed

Prep and cook time: 20 mins | Difficulty: easy

Ingredients (for 4 servings)
1tbsp instant dashi (Japanese stock), or a good stock cube
800ml | 3½ cups water
2tbsp miso paste
2 potatoes, peeled and diced
35g | ¼ cup dried seaweed
1tsp soy sauce
200g | 8oz tofu
6 spring onions, sliced

Method
1 Mix the dashi with the water and miso paste and bring to the boil.
2 Add the potatoes and simmer for about 15 minutes or until potatoes are very nearly tender.
3 Add the seaweed, soy sauce, tofu and spring onions and serve piping hot.

Per serving: Cals 149 Fat 2.5g Sat fat 0.5g Protein 7.2g

rice salad with tuna, red onions and egg

Prep and cook time: 45 mins | Difficulty: easy

Ingredients (for 4 servings)
200g | 2 cups long-grain rice
2 cloves garlic, finely chopped
300g | 1½ cups tinned tuna, drained of oil and flaked
2tbsp olive oil
1tbsp white wine vinegar
Salt and pepper to taste
2 red onions, sliced into rings
2 medium eggs, hard boiled
1 bunch dill, sprigged

Method
1 Cook the rice in plenty of boiling water according to the packet instructions, then drain and rinse in cold water.
2 Mix together the tuna and garlic, then mix with the rice.
3 Mix the oil with the vinegar and season with salt and pepper.
4 Stir into the rice mixture and let stand for about 20 minutes.
5 Pile the salad onto plates. Peel the eggs and cut into quarters, lay onto the salad and scatter over the red onion rings and the dill.

Per serving: Cals 314 Fat 10.2g Sat fat 2g Protein 25g

chicken kebabs with tabouleh

salad niçoise

Prep and cook time: 30 mins | Difficulty: easy

Ingredients (for 4 servings)
For the dressing:
1 shallot, very finely chopped
2tbsp white wine vinegar
½tbsp grain mustard
4tbsp olive oil
Salt and pepper to taste

For the salad:
400g | 1lb new potatoes
200g | 8oz cherry tomatoes
200g | 8oz green beans
200g | 8oz tinned tuna, drained of oil
100g | 1 cup pitted black olives
4 tinned anchovies, sliced thinly into strips
1 handful rocket, washed
Mint, to garnish

Method

1 Make the dressing: mix the ingredients together, season with salt and pepper and set aside.
2 Heat the oven to 200ºC/400ºF/Gas Mark 6.
3 Bring a large pan of salted water to a boil and cook the potatoes until tender. Drain well and set aside. Cut potatoes in half if they are large.
4 Put the tomatoes in a roasting tin and roast for 10 minutes.
5 Blanch the beans in boiling water for 5 minutes, drain and refresh in cold water. Pat dry with kitchen paper.
6 While the potatoes are still slightly warm, combine all the ingredients and toss in the dressing. Garnish with mint leaves.

Per serving: Cals **295** Fat **15.2g** Sat fat **1.75g** Protein **16.9g**

pumpkin soup with sour cream

Prep and cook time: 1 hour 20 mins | Difficulty: easy

Ingredients (for 4 servings)
800g | 2lb pumpkin or squash, peeled and seeds removed
1tbsp olive oil
1 onion, chopped
2 cloves garlic, chopped
1tsp curry powder
1tsp ground ginger
1 apple, peeled, cored and chopped
50ml | 10tsp dry sherry
800ml | 3½ cups vegetable stock
250ml | 1 cup reduced-fat sour cream
Salt and pepper to taste

Method

1 Preheat the oven to 200ºC/400ºF/Gas Mark 6.
2 Cut about 100g of the pumpkin flesh into very thin strips and chop the remainder.
3 Place the pumpkin strips onto a baking tray and roast in the oven for about 30 minutes, turning occasionally.
4 Meanwhile, heat the oil in a large non-stick pan and gently cook the onion until translucent. Add the garlic, curry powder and ginger and cook for 2 minutes.
5 Stir in the apple and chopped pumpkin and cook gently for 5 minutes. Add the sherry, let it bubble then pour in the stock.
6 Bring to a boil and simmer for 20 minutes. Stir in 200ml of the sour cream and whizz in a blender until smooth.
7 Pass through a fine sieve, return to the pan and gently reheat. Season with salt and pepper.
8 Serve the soup garnished with the remaining sour cream and roasted pumpkin.

Per serving: Cals **249** Fat **11.8g** Sat fat **4.6g** Protein **4.4g**

pumpkin soup with sour cream

open sandwich of turkey breast, avocado and cheese

open sandwich of turkey breast, avocado and cheese

Prep and cook time: 10 mins | Difficulty: easy

Ingredients (for 4 servings)
4 slices wholemeal bread
6 lettuce leaves, washed and torn
50g | 2oz Cheddar cheese, finely sliced
1 avocado, peeled, stone removed and chopped
300g | 12oz turkey breast, cooked and sliced
Salt and pepper to taste

Method
1 Top each slice of bread with lettuce, cheese, avocado and turkey and season with salt and pepper.

Per serving: Cals **288** Fat **14g** Sat fat **4g** Protein **21g**

chickpea and spinach salad

Prep and cook time: 30 mins | Difficulty: easy

Ingredients (for 4 servings)
2 red peppers
2tbsp olive oil
½tsp English mustard
½ pinch sugar
1tbsp cider vinegar
Salt and pepper to taste
500g | 6 cups baby spinach
400g | 2 cups tinned chickpeas, drained and rinsed
1 avocado, peeled, stone removed and chopped
2 large tomatoes, deseeded and chopped
8 green olives, pitted and chopped
3 spring onions, finely chopped
2tbsp parsley, chopped

Method
1 Put the peppers under a hot grill and grill on all sides until the skin has blackened. Put in a large bowl, cover with cling film and set aside.
2 Mix the oil, mustard, sugar and vinegar and season with salt and pepper.
3 When the peppers are cool enough to handle, remove the skins and discard the seeds. Chop the flesh.
4 Gently mix the peppers with the rest of the ingredients, toss with the dressing and serve.

Per serving: Cals **312** Fat **17g** Sat fat **2g** Protein **9g**

vegetable stew with cabbage and chickpeas

Prep and cook time: 40 mins | Difficulty: easy

Ingredients (for 4 servings)
1tbsp olive oil
2 shallots, finely chopped
2 cloves garlic, finely chopped
1 small Savoy cabbage, stem removed and coarsely shredded
1tbsp tomato purée
600ml | 2½ cups vegetable stock
200g | 1 cup canned chickpeas, drained and rinsed
2 tomatoes, finely chopped
1tsp fresh ginger, peeled and grated
1 red chilli, deseeded and finely chopped
25g | ¼ cup Parmesan cheese, roughly grated
Salt and pepper to taste

Method
1 Heat the oil in a deep pan and fry the shallots and the garlic for a couple of minutes.
2 Add the cabbage and fry gently for about 2 minutes.
3 Stir in the tomato purée and the stock.
4 Add the chickpeas, tomatoes, ginger and chilli and simmer covered for 20 minutes, stirring occasionally.
5 Season with salt and pepper and serve with grated Parmesan.

Per serving: Cals **174** Fat **6g** Sat fat **1.5g** Protein **7.1g**

thai tom yum soup

Prep and cook time: 25 mins | Difficulty: easy

Ingredients (for 4 servings)
1L | 4 cups beef stock
2 kaffir lime leaves
1 stalk lemongrass, crushed
1 thumb-sized piece fresh ginger, peeled and sliced
1tsp tamarind concentrate
400g | 1lb green beans, trimmed
4 chicken legs, boned and chopped
2 red chillies, sliced
1 tin baby corn, drained and rinsed
1tbsp fish sauce
1tbsp chilli sauce
Pea shoots, to garnish

Method
1 Put the beef stock into a pan with the kaffir lime leaves, crushed
  lemongrass, ginger and tamarind concentrate and bring to the boil.
2 Add the beans and simmer gently for 2-3 minutes. Add the chicken,
  chilli and baby corn and simmer for a further 5-6 minutes, or until the
  chicken is cooked.
3 Season with fish sauce and chilli sauce. Remove the lemongrass and
  serve garnished with pea shoots.

Per serving: Cals **205** Fat **4.1g** Sat fat **0g** Protein **26.7g**

creamed lentil soup with ceps

Prep and cook time: 50 mins | Soaking time: 1 hour
Difficulty: easy

Ingredients (for 4 servings)
100g | 4oz dried mushrooms
300g | 1½ cups green Puy lentils
1L | 4 cups vegetable stock
2 onions, chopped
2 cloves garlic, chopped
150g | 1 cup celeriac, peeled and diced
2 carrots, peeled and diced
2 sprigs thyme
250ml | 1 cup red wine
150ml | ⅔ cup single cream
1 large cooking apple, peeled and sliced
200g | 2 cups fresh ceps, sliced
1tbsp balsamic vinegar
Salt and pepper to taste

Method
1 Soak the dried mushrooms in about 300ml warm water for 1 hour.
2 Wash the lentils, put into a pan with the vegetable stock and cook for
  about 20 minutes. Take out about ¼ of the lentils with a slotted spoon
  and set aside.
3 In a non-stick frying pan cook the onions until translucent then add
  the garlic. Add the diced vegetables and thyme and stir in the wine.
  Add the dried mushrooms and their soaking juice and cook gently for
  about 10 minutes.
4 Add the vegetable mixture to the lentils and stock and cook for
  a further 10 minutes or so. Add the cream and season with salt
  and pepper.
5 Purée with a hand blender, push through a fine sieve then put the
  reserved lentils back into the soup.
6 Heat a non-stick frying pan and lightly brown first the ceps and then
  the apple slices.
7 Ladle the soup into 4 bowls, put a few slices of apple and ceps into
  each and sprinkle with balsamic vinegar.

Per serving: Cals **408** Fat **8.4g** Sat fat **4.5g** Protein **12.4g**

lemon couscous with peppers and olives

Prep and cook time: 30 mins | Difficulty: easy

Ingredients (for 4 servings)
300g | 2 cups couscous
1tbsp olive oil
2 shallots, finely chopped
2 cloves garlic, finely chopped
4 preserved lemons, roughly chopped
1 red pepper, deseeded and chopped
125g | 1 cup black olives, stoned
Salt and pepper to taste
Juice of 1 lemon
2tbsp fresh coriander, chopped

Method

1 Cook the couscous according to packet instructions and keep warm.
2 Heat the oil and cook the garlic and shallots until translucent. Add the chopped lemon, red pepper and olives and stir briefly. Transfer to a bowl and mix with the lemon juice.
3 Season well with salt and pepper, mix in the chopped coriander and carefully stir in the couscous. Leave to stand for at least 1 hour before serving.

Per serving: Cals **188** Fat **6g** Sat fat **0.5g** Protein **2.8g**

quinoa salad with black olives and feta cheese

Prep and cook time: 30 mins | Difficulty: easy

Ingredients (for 4 servings)
200g | 1 cup quinoa
100g | 1 cup feta cheese, diced
1 red onion, sliced
½ cucumber, chopped
4 tomatoes, chopped
200g | 2 cups black olives
25g | 1 cup parsley, chopped
1tbsp olive oil
Salt and pepper to taste
Watercress, to garnish

Method

1 Cook quinoa according to packet instructions. Drain well and rinse.
2 Combine the quinoa with the other ingredients, season with salt and pepper and serve garnished with the watercress.

Per serving: Cals **358** Fat **19.1g** Sat fat **6g** Protein **13.3g**

spinach and sprout salad with chilli sauce and feta cheese

spinach and sprout salad with chilli sauce and feta cheese

Prep and cook time: 15 mins | Difficulty: easy

Ingredients (for 4 servings)
2tbsp chilli sauce
1tbsp sesame oil
Juice of 2 limes
Salt and pepper to taste
2 carrots, peeled and grated
200g | 2 cups young spinach, washed and torn
150g | 1½ cups mixed sprouting beans
100g | 1 cup black olives, chopped
100g | 1 cup feta cheese, crumbled

Method
1 Mix the chilli sauce with the sesame oil and lime juice and season with salt and pepper.
2 Mix together the grated carrots, spinach, sprouting beans and olives and arrange on plates.
3 Scatter with the feta cheese, drizzle with the dressing and serve.

Per serving: Cals **177** Fat **11.3g** Sat fat **4.2g** Protein **5.5g**

rice with lentils and caramelised onions

Prep and cook time: 45 mins | Difficulty: easy

Ingredients (for 4 servings)
400g | 2 cups basmati rice
200g | 1 cup brown lentils
2 onions, finely sliced
1tbsp olive oil
1 pinch ground allspice
1 pinch curry powder
Salt and pepper to taste
1tbsp light soy sauce

Method
1 Cook the rice according to the packet instructions, rinse in cold water and drain.
2 Cook the lentils according to the packet instructions, rinse in cold water and drain.
3 Heat the oil in a frying pan and slowly fry the onions, stirring occasionally, until golden brown and caramelised. Stir in the allspice and curry powder and cook for 2 minutes.
4 Add the rice and lentils and fry all together for about 3-4 minutes. Add salt, pepper and soy sauce to taste and serve.

Per serving: Cals **218** Fat **4.1g** Sat fat **0.5g** Protein **5.5g**

minestrone soup

Prep and cook time: 35 mins | Difficulty: easy

Ingredients (for 4 servings)
4 tomatoes
1tbsp olive oil
2 onions, finely chopped
2 carrots, finely diced
2 small courgettes, finely diced
2 cloves garlic, peeled and crushed
250g | 2 cups passata (sieved tomatoes)
600ml | 2½ cups vegetable stock
600g | 3 cups butter beans, canned
Salt and pepper to taste
25g | ½ cup Parmesan cheese, grated
Wholewheat bread to serve

Method
1 Drop the tomatoes into boiling water for a few seconds, then skin, halve, deseed and finely dice.
2 Heat the oil in a pan and gently cook the onions until translucent then add the carrots, courgettes and garlic and cook for 2-3 minutes, stirring.
3 Add the passata. Cook over a very low heat until reduced slightly, then add the stock.
4 Bring to the boil, stir in the diced tomato and simmer over a low heat for about 10 minutes.
5 Stir in the drained beans and cook gently for a further couple of minutes.
6 Season to taste with salt and pepper. Sprinkle with Parmesan and serve with wholewheat bread (not included in nutritional values).

Per serving: Cals **345** Fat **7.3g** Sat fat **2.6g** Protein **17.3g**

carrot and lentil soup

Prep and cook time: 40 mins | Difficulty: easy

Ingredients (for 4 servings)
1tbsp cumin seeds
1tbsp olive oil
600g | 1½lb carrots, peeled and chopped
150g | ¾ cup split red lentils, rinsed
½tsp chilli flakes
1.2L | 5 cups vegetable stock or water
125ml | ½ cup semi-skimmed milk
Salt and pepper to taste
Lime zest, to garnish

Method
1 Heat a non-stick frying pan and dry roast the cumin seeds until they start to colour. Remove from the pan and set aside.
2 Heat the oil in the pan and gently cook the carrots for about 3 minutes or until they start to soften.
3 Stir in the lentils and the chilli flakes then add the stock or water and bring to a boil. Simmer for 20-30 minutes, or until the lentils and carrots are cooked through.
4 Add the milk then whizz in a blender until smooth. Pass through a fine sieve, return to the pan and gently reheat. Season with salt and pepper and serve garnished with the lime zest.

Per serving: Cals **342** Fat **4.9g** Sat fat **0.9g** Protein **13.7g**

minestrone soup

lentil salad with pumpkin and goats' cheese

Prep and cook time: 45 mins | Difficulty: easy

Ingredients (for 4 servings)
800g | 2lb pumpkin, skinned, seeds removed and cubed
3tbsp olive oil
2 cloves garlic, crushed
400g | 2 cups tinned lentils, drained and rinsed
1 bunch rocket
150g | ⅔ cup hard goats' cheese, chopped
2tbsp cider vinegar
1tsp balsamic vinegar
Salt and pepper to taste

Method
1 Blanch the pumpkin in boiling salted water for about 5 minutes. Drain and pat dry.
2 Heat 1 tablespoon of oil in a large pan and gently fry the garlic. Add the pumpkin and cook until tender and starting to brown.
3 Arrange the lentils on plates with the pumpkin, rocket and goats' cheese.
4 Mix together the remaining oil, cider vinegar and balsamic vinegar. Season and drizzle over the salad.

Per serving: Cals **308** Fat **6.5g** Sat fat **5.6g** Protein **13.2g**

rice with spinach and sweet potatoes

Prep and cook time: 40 mins | Difficulty: medium

Ingredients (for 4 servings)
1tbsp olive oil
1 leek, finely chopped
2 cloves garlic, chopped
800ml | 3½ cups vegetable stock
400g | 2 cups rice, rinsed
2 pinches saffron
2 sweet potatoes, peeled and finely diced
200g | 1 cup tinned chickpeas, drained and rinsed
200g | 8oz spinach, washed and stalks removed
Salt and pepper to taste

Method
1 Heat the oil in a large pan and gently cook the leeks and garlic for 5 minutes.
2 Add the stock, bring to the boil then add the rice and the saffron. Simmer gently for 10 minutes.
3 Add the sweet potato and chickpeas and simmer for 15 minutes or until the rice has absorbed most of the liquid. Add a little water if necessary.
4 Tear the spinach and add to the pan, cook for 2 minutes then season with salt and pepper and serve.

Per serving: Cals **255** Fat **4g** Sat fat **0.5g** Protein **6.2g**

lentil salad with pumpkin and goats' cheese

chicken kebabs with lemon dip

Prep and cook time: 30 mins | Marinade: 30 mins | Difficulty: easy

Ingredients (for 4 servings)
4 chicken breasts, skinned
1tsp dried thyme
1tsp ground coriander
1tsp ground cumin
2tbsp olive oil
Salt and pepper to taste
4 red onions, peeled and cut into wedges
8 wooden skewers, soaked

For the dip:
4tbsp low-fat crème fraîche
Zest of ½ lemon
1 clove garlic, crushed

Method
1 Dice the chicken breasts and mix with the thyme, coriander, cumin and oil. Season with salt and pepper and set aside to marinate for 30 minutes.
2 Thread the onions and chicken on wooden skewers and grill for about 6 minutes, turning and basting as they cook.
3 For the dip: mix the crème fraîche with the lemon zest and garlic. Season to taste.
4 Arrange the kebabs on a platter. Put the dip into a small bowl and place on the platter to serve.

Per serving: Cals **286** Fat **9.8g** Sat fat **1g** Protein **26g**

asparagus and poached egg on toast

Prep and cook time: 30 mins | Difficulty: easy

Ingredients (for 4 servings)
400g | 1lb asparagus, trimmed
2tbsp olive oil
2tbsp mint leaves, chopped
4 medium eggs
4 slices wholemeal bread
Salt and pepper to taste

Method
1 Bring a large pan of salted water to a boil and cook the asparagus until just tender. Drain well and keep warm.
2 Meanwhile, warm the oil in a pan, stir in the mint leaves and set aside.
3 Fill a wide pan with about 8cm/3in water and bring it to a boil.
4 Turn the heat down so only a few bubbles rise to the surface. Break the eggs into individual cups and carefully slip into the water.
5 Cook for about 3 minutes then remove from the pan with a slotted spoon.
6 Toast the bread, lay on the asparagus then the egg and pour over the mint oil. Season with salt and pepper and serve immediately.

Per serving: Cals **218** Fat **13g** Sat fat **3g** Protein **10g**

asparagus and poached egg on toast

smoked trout and fennel salad

Prep and cook time: 10 mins | Difficulty: easy

Ingredients (for 4 servings)
200g | 8oz French beans
1 bulb fennel, thinly sliced
1 red onion, thinly sliced
4 smoked trout fillets, flaked
2tbsp capers
2 sprigs dill, chopped
3tbsp olive oil
1tbsp white wine vinegar
2tsp wholegrain mustard

Method
1 Cut the ends off the beans and plunge them into boiling water for 2
minutes. Drain, refresh under cold running water and gently pat dry
with kitchen paper.
2 Put the fennel and onion into a bowl and add the smoked trout,
capers, dill and French beans.
3 Mix the oil, vinegar and mustard in a small bowl, season to taste with
salt and pepper and dress the salad. Serve immediately.

Per serving: Cals **292** Fat **18.5g** Sat fat **2.5g** Protein **24.2g**

honey and soy glazed sesame tofu

Prep and cook time: 15 mins | Marinade: 2 hours | Difficulty: easy

Ingredients (for 4 servings)
2 limes
2tbsp honey
2tbsp soy sauce
2tbsp sesame oil
400g | 1lb firm tofu, cubed
1tbsp sesame seeds
8 wooden skewers, soaked

Method
1 Peel the limes with a very sharp knife and cut the peel into strips.
Squeeze the juice from the fruit.
2 Whisk together the honey, soy sauce, lime juice and sesame oil. Mix
with the tofu and leave to marinate for 2 hours.
3 Thread the tofu onto wooden skewers. Grill the kebabs for about 2
minutes each side, turning and basting as they cook.
4 Sprinkle with sesame seeds and serve garnished with lime curls.

Per serving: Cals **178** Fat **11.3g** Sat fat **2g** Protein **8g**

smoked trout and fennel salad

gazpacho

gazpacho

Prep and cook time: 20 mins | Chilling: 1 hour | Difficulty: easy

Ingredients (for 4 servings)
500g | 1lb ripe tomatoes
½ cucumber, peeled and finely diced
1 red pepper, deseeded and finely diced
2 Spanish onions
1tbsp white wine vinegar
2 cloves garlic, crushed
1tsp sugar
1tsp sweet paprika
1tbsp ground almonds
2tbsp olive oil
Salt and pepper to taste

Method

1 Put the tomatoes into a bowl and cover with boiling water. Let sit for 1 minute then remove the skins.
2 Set aside 1 tablespoon of the cucumber and 1 tablespoon of the pepper for garnishing.
3 Put all the ingredients into a blender and blend until smooth, adding enough cold water to make the required consistency.
4 Season with salt and pepper – you may also want to add more sugar.
5 Chill for at least an hour then serve in 4 glasses with the reserved diced cucumber and red pepper as a garnish.

Per serving: Cals **140** Fat **7g** Sat fat **1g** Protein **1.5g**

rice and pepper salad with grilled chicken breast

Prep and cook time: 45 mins | Difficulty: easy

Ingredients (for 4 servings)
200g | 1 cup long-grain rice
400ml | 1⅔ cups vegetable stock
½tsp turmeric
3tbsp olive oil
1tsp chilli powder
2 red peppers, deseeded and chopped
4tbsp lime juice
Salt and freshly ground black pepper to taste
4 chicken breasts, skinned
1tbsp sunflower oil
Fresh coriander, to garnish

Method

1 Rinse the rice and put into a large pan with the stock and turmeric. Bring to a boil and cook until the rice is tender and the stock has been absorbed. Fluff up with a fork.
2 Heat 1 tablespoon of oil in a frying pan, add the chilli powder, cook for 2 minutes then add the peppers. Cook for 10 minutes or until tender, stirring from time to time.
3 Season the lime juice with salt and freshly ground pepper and whisk in the remaining oil to make a dressing.
4 Mix the peppers into the rice and stir in the dressing. Season with salt and pepper to taste.
5 Season the chicken breasts with pepper and rub with the sunflower oil. Heat a griddle pan until very hot, then cook the chicken for about 5 minutes on each side or until cooked through.
6 Spoon the salad onto plates, slice the chicken at an angle and arrange on top of the salad. Serve garnished with coriander.

Per serving: Cals **318** Fat **15.9g** Sat fat **1.8g** Protein **25.8g**

quinoa salad with pumpkin and feta

Prep and cook time: 25 mins | Difficulty: easy

Ingredients (for 4 servings)
200 g | 1 cup quinoa
1kg | 2lb pumpkin or squash, peeled, seeds removed and cubed
100g | 1 cup feta cheese, crumbled
2 handfuls baby spinach

For the dressing:
2tbsp olive oil
2tbsp cider vinegar
2tsp honey
Salt and pepper to taste

Method
1 Preheat the oven to 200°C/400°F/Gas Mark 6.
2 Place the pumpkin onto a baking tray and roast in the oven for about 30 minutes, turning occasionally.
3 Cook the quinoa according to packet instructions. Drain, rinse and set aside.
4 To make the dressing, whisk together the oil, vinegar and honey and season to taste.
5 Combine the salad ingredients, toss with the dressing and serve.

Per serving: Cals **383** Fat **17.7g** Sat fat **6.5g** Protein **14.4g**

sweetcorn soup with chilli

Prep and cook time: 35 mins | Difficulty: easy

Ingredients (for 4 servings)
1tbsp olive oil
2 onions, finely chopped
1 clove garlic, finely chopped
1 chilli pepper, cut into rings
300g | 10½oz floury potatoes, peeled and cubed
2tbsp cornflour
100ml | 7tbsp white wine
500ml | 2 cups vegetable stock
300ml | 1⅓ cups semi-skimmed milk
4 fresh bay leaves
400g sweetcorn, frozen or tinned
Salt and freshly cracked pepper to taste

Method
1 Heat the oil in a pan. Add the onions, garlic, chilli and potatoes and sweat for a few minutes. Add the cornflour and stir to coat.
2 Pour in the white wine and the vegetable stock, bring to a boil and simmer for about 20 minutes.
3 Pour in the milk and add the bay leaves and sweetcorn. Simmer gently on a low heat for a few minutes, then season to taste with salt and pepper and serve.

Per serving: Cals **271** Fat **6.5g** Sat fat **2g** Protein **7.8g**

quinoa salad with pumpkin and feta

haricot beans and tomatoes on ciabatta

Prep and cook time: 20 mins | Difficulty: easy

Ingredients (for 4 sandwiches)
Juice and zest of 1 lemon
4tbsp olive oil
1 clove garlic, crushed
200g | 2 cups canned haricot beans, drained and rinsed
1 red onion, finely chopped
2tbsp parsley, finely chopped
4 bunches vine tomatoes
8 slices rustic Italian white bread, or ciabatta
1 clove garlic, whole
2 handfuls rocket, washed and dried
Salt and pepper to taste

Method
1 Heat the oven to 200°C/400°F/Gas Mark 6.
2 Mix the lemon juice, oil and crushed garlic and season with
  salt and pepper.
3 Mix the haricot beans, red onion, lemon zest and parsley and
  stir in the dressing.
4 Put the tomatoes into the oven and roast for 15 minutes.
  Toast the bread and rub with the whole garlic clove.
5 Pile spoonfuls of the vegetable mixture on each slice and top with
  rocket and tomatoes. Serve immediately.

Per serving: Cals 413 Fat 16.7g Sat fat 4g Protein 11.6g

chicken, mushroom and garlic wraps

Prep and cook time: 30 mins | Difficulty: easy

Ingredients (for 4 wraps)
4 flour tortilla wraps
1tbsp olive oil
½ small onion, finely chopped
½ clove garlic, crushed
100g | 4oz button mushrooms, thinly sliced
2 chicken breasts, skinned and cubed
100ml | ¾ cup barbecue sauce

Method
1 Heat the oven to a low setting, put the wraps on a baking sheet and
  put in the oven to warm through.
2 Heat the oil in a pan and gently cook the onion until translucent,
  then add the garlic and cook for 1 minute.
3 Stir in the mushrooms with a splash of water, let it bubble then add
  the cubed chicken and cook for about 5 minutes.
4 Stir in the barbecue sauce, heat for 2 minutes then spoon the
  mixture onto the warmed wraps.

Per serving: Cals 345 Fat 9.8g Sat fat 2.6g Protein 23.2g

haricot beans and tomatoes on ciabatta

smoked mackerel salad with potatoes

Prep and cook time: 10 mins | Difficulty: easy

Ingredients (for 4 servings)
2 small courgettes, washed, trimmed and sliced on an angle
into 2cm lengths
16 small new potatoes, cooked and halved
100g | 4 cups mixed salad leaves of your choice
3 sprigs parsley, roughly chopped
2 sprigs tarragon, roughly chopped
300g | 1½ cups smoked mackerel, flaked

For the dressing:
1tbsp white wine vinegar
2tbsp olive oil
Salt and pepper to taste

Method
1 Blanch the courgettes in boiling, salted water for 2 minutes.
  Drain and refresh in ice-cold water.
2 Gently mix the courgettes with the potatoes, leaves, herbs and
  flaked fish.
3 Mix the oil and vinegar, season with salt and pepper and toss into
  the salad ingredients.

Per serving: Cals **391** Fat **27g** Sat fat **6.2g** Protein **18.5g**

tomato and pepper soup with kidney beans

Prep and cook time: 30 mins | Difficulty: easy

Ingredients (for 4 servings)
1tbsp olive oil
1 onion, finely chopped
2 cloves garlic, chopped
4 red peppers, deseeded and chopped
400g | 2 cups tinned tomatoes, chopped
500ml | 2 cups vegetable stock or water
2tsp dried oregano
400g | 2 cups tinned kidney beans, drained and rinsed
2tbsp Worcestershire sauce
1tsp sugar
Salt and pepper to taste

To garnish:
50g | ½ cup Parmesan cheese, grated
2tbsp chopped parsley

Method
1 Heat the oil in a pan and gently cook the onion until translucent.
2 Add the garlic and red peppers and cook slowly for about 10 minutes.
3 Add the tomatoes and stock, cook for 10 more minutes then add the
  oregano, kidney beans, Worcestershire sauce and sugar.
4 Let simmer for another 10 minutes, season with salt and pepper
  and serve with the Parmesan and parsley.

Per serving: Cals **251** Fat **8.2g** Sat fat **2.6g** Protein **3.5g**

smoked mackerel salad with potatoes

tomato salad with beans and cottage cheese

Prep and cook time: 15 mins | Difficulty: easy

Ingredients (for 4 servings)
2tbsp olive oil
1tbsp white wine vinegar
Pinch of salt and pepper
400g | 2 cups tinned butter beans, drained and rinsed
400g | 1lb cherry tomatoes, halved
1 red onion, finely sliced
200g | 1 cup cottage cheese, drained
2tbsp chopped basil
2tbsp chopped mint

Method
1 Mix together the oil and vinegar and season with salt and pepper.
2 Combine the rest of the ingredients and carefully stir in the dressing.

Per serving: Cals **254** Fat **9.4g** Sat fat **2.9g** Protein **13g**

basil and tomato bruschetta

Prep and cook time: 20 mins | Difficulty: easy

Ingredients (for 4 servings)
8 medium tomatoes
25g | 1 cup basil
2tbsp olive oil
Salt and pepper to taste
8 slices French bread

Method
1 Cut the tomatoes in half, scrape out the seeds and roughly chop the flesh.
2 Reserve a few basil leaves for garnish then chop the rest of the leaves.
3 Mix the tomatoes with the oil and basil and season with salt and pepper.
4 Toast or grill the slices of bread and serve topped with the tomato mixture. Garnish with the reserved basil leaves.

Per serving: Cals **305** Fat **10.1g** Sat fat **1g** Protein **8g**

tomato salad with beans and cottage cheese

spinach and chicken salad with sesame

Prep and cook time: 25 mins | Difficulty: easy

Ingredients (for 4 servings)
4 chicken breasts, cut into bite-sized pieces
2tbsp light soy sauce
4tbsp sesame oil
2tbsp rice wine vinegar
Salt and pepper to taste
1 red pepper, deseeded and finely sliced
400g | 1lb baby spinach, washed
2 nori leaves, shredded
2tbsp sesame seeds

Method

1 Mix the chicken pieces with the soy sauce and allow to marinate for 20 minutes.
2 Mix the sesame oil and rice wine vinegar, season with salt and pepper and set aside.
3 Put the chicken into a non-stick wok, then stir-fry for 3 minutes or until lightly browned.
4 Mix the spinach with the pepper and toss into the oil and vinegar dressing. Add more seasoning if desired.
5 Carefully toss the chicken with the spinach. Arrange the salad mixture on plates.
6 Garnish with the nori strips, sprinkle with the sesame seeds and serve immediately.

Per serving: Cals 292 Fat 16.8g Sat fat 2.1g Protein 27.8g

red lentil soup with fresh coriander

Prep and cook time: 40 mins | Difficulty: easy

Ingredients (for 4 servings)
1tbsp sesame oil
1 onion, chopped
1tbsp fresh ginger, peeled and grated
1 fennel bulb, trimmed and finely chopped
2 red chillies, deseeded and finely chopped
1tsp curry powder
400g | 3 cups red lentils
1L | 4 cups vegetable stock
4 sprigs fresh coriander, to garnish
Lemon wedges, to garnish
Salt and pepper to taste

Method

1 Heat the oil in a large pan and cook the onion, ginger, fennel and chillies until softened.
2 Add the curry powder and cook for 2 minutes then stir in the lentils and add the stock. Cover and simmer over a low heat for about 20 minutes, or until cooked.
3 Take 2 ladles of lentils out of the soup and finely purée the rest of the soup. Return the whole lentils to the soup.
4 Season with salt and pepper. Ladle into cups or bowls and serve garnished with fresh coriander and lemon wedges.

Per serving: Cals 191 Fat 3.9g Sat fat 0.5g Protein 9g

chicken breast with spinach
and stewed peppers

dinner

chicken breast with spinach and stewed peppers

Prep and cook time: 30 mins | Difficulty: easy

Ingredients (for 4 servings)
200g | 1 cup quinoa
2tbsp olive oil
2 cloves garlic, crushed
1 red chilli, deseeded and finely chopped
4 red peppers, deseeded and chopped
2 tomatoes, chopped
Salt and pepper to taste
400g | 1lb spinach, washed
4 chicken breasts, skinned

Method

1 Cook the quinoa according to packet instructions and keep warm.
2 Meanwhile, make the sauce. Heat 1 tablespoon of oil in a pan and gently cook the garlic and chilli for 2 minutes, stirring all the time.
3 Add the peppers, cook for 5 minutes; then add the tomatoes, reduce the heat and simmer for 20 minutes. Season with salt and pepper.
4 Put the wet spinach in a large pan with a lid on, and cook until it wilts. Drain well, squeeze out any excess moisture and keep warm.
5 Put the chicken breasts between two sheets of cling film and bash with a rolling pin to flatten.
6 Heat the remaining oil in a wide pan, cook the chicken breasts until lightly brown on one side. Remove from the pan, put a little spinach on the cooked side of each one and secure with a cocktail stick.
7 Return to the pan carefully and cook gently for about 5 minutes or until the chicken is cooked through.
8 Serve on a bed of quinoa and pepper sauce.

Per serving: Cals **236** Fat **11.7g** Sat fat **1g** Protein **35.2g**

grilled tuna steaks with kidney bean and tomato salad

Prep and cook time: 30 mins | Difficulty: easy

Ingredients (for 4 servings)
200g | 1 cup red kidney beans, tinned
1 red onion, finely chopped
1 green pepper, deseeded and finely chopped
1 red pepper, deseeded and finely chopped
3 tomatoes, deseeded and finely chopped
2tbsp olive oil
Juice and zest of 1 lime
1 clove garlic, finely chopped
Salt and pepper to taste
4 tuna steaks
1tbsp parsley, finely chopped
1tbsp mint, finely chopped

To garnish:
Mint leaves
4 lime wedges

Method

1 Drain the kidney beans and rinse under running water.
2 Mix together the beans, red onion, peppers, tomatoes, 1 tablespoon of olive oil and lime juice in a bowl and set aside.
3 Mix the garlic with the remaining olive oil and add the lime zest. Season with salt and pepper.
4 Brush the fish with the lime oil and grill for about 3 minutes each side, or till cooked to your liking.
5 Mix the parsley and mint into the bean salad and season to taste.
6 Arrange the tuna and salad on plates. Garnish with the mint leaves and lime wedges and serve.

Per serving: Cals **483** Fat **18.5g** Sat fat **4g** Protein **57.8g**

grilled tuna steaks with
kidney bean and tomato salad

sesame chicken with asparagus and tomatoes

Prep and cook time: 30 mins | Marinade: 1 hour | Difficulty: easy

Ingredients (for 4 servings)
2tbsp sesame oil
2tbsp sesame seeds
3tbsp Marsala or dry sherry
1 clove garlic, crushed
2 chicken breasts, skinned and cubed
200g | 8oz asparagus, trimmed
2 onions, cut into wedges
6 tomatoes, deseeded and chopped
Sesame seeds, to garnish
Coriander leaves, to garnish

Method
1 Mix the oil with the sesame seeds, Marsala and garlic and stir into the cubed chicken. Set aside to marinate for 1 hour.
2 Bring a large pan of salted water to a boil and blanch the asparagus for 3 minutes. Drain, refresh under cold running water, pat dry with kitchen paper and cut into 4cm lengths.
3 Remove the chicken from the marinade and add to a smoking wok. Stir-fry for 1 minute then add the onion and cook for about 3 minutes, stirring all the time.
4 Add the tomatoes and asparagus, cook for 2 minutes then add a little of the marinade and cook for 1 more minute.
5 Serve immediately with sesame seeds and coriander leaves to garnish.

Per serving: Cals **240** Fat **23.6g** Sat fat **1.7g** Protein **19g**

salmon fillet on pak choi

Prep and cook time: 40 mins | Difficulty: easy

Ingredients (for 4 servings)
300g | 1½ cups basmati rice
4 pak choi
25g | 1 cup fresh coriander, finely chopped
Zest and juice of 2 limes
Salt and pepper to taste
4 salmon fillets
4 squares of tinfoil

Method
1 Preheat the oven to 180°C/350°F/Gas Mark 4.
2 Cook rice according to the packet instructions and keep warm.
3 Cut the pak choi in half lengthways and blanch in a large pan of boiling salted water for 3 minutes. Drain well and keep warm.
4 Mix the coriander with the lime zest and juice, then season with salt and pepper.
5 Spread the coriander mixture over the salmon fillets and seal each piece in a square of tinfoil. Bake on a tray in the oven for 20 minutes or until cooked through.
6 Arrange the salmon on the rice and pak choi and serve immediately.

Per serving: Cals **448** Fat **18g** Sat fat **3g** Protein **42g**

chicken breast with red quinoa salad

Prep and cook time: 30 mins | Marinade: 30 mins | Difficulty: easy

Ingredients (for 4 servings)
4 chicken breasts, skinned
1tbsp olive oil
1 clove garlic, finely chopped
1tsp ground cumin
Salt and pepper to taste

For the salad:
200g | 1 cup red quinoa
1 red onion, sliced
1 red pepper, deseeded and sliced
1 yellow pepper, deseeded and sliced
400g | 2 cups tinned chickpeas, drained and rinsed
1tbsp olive oil
1tbsp white wine vinegar

To serve:
4 handfuls lamb's lettuce

Method

1 Mix together the oil, garlic and cumin, season with salt and pepper and rub into the chicken breasts. Leave to marinate for 30 minutes.
2 Cook the quinoa according to packet instructions. Drain and rinse under running water.
3 Mix the quinoa with the onion, peppers and chickpeas. Mix together the olive oil and vinegar, season with salt and pepper and then stir into the salad.
4 Fry the chicken in a non-stick pan for 5 minutes on each side or until cooked through.
5 Slice the chicken breasts and serve on the lamb's lettuce with the quinoa salad alongside.

Per serving: Cals **450** Fat **13.3g** Sat fat **1.5g** Protein **35g**

sesame seed salmon with green beans and asparagus

Prep and cook time: 30 mins | Difficulty: medium

Ingredients (for 4 servings)
4tbsp sesame oil
2tbsp sesame seeds
4tbsp soy sauce
4tbsp honey
4 pieces salmon fillet
400g | 1lb asparagus, trimmed
400g | 1lb green beans, trimmed

Method

1 Mix 2 tablespoons oil with the sesame seeds, soy sauce and honey. Coat the fish with the mixture and set aside.
2 Bring a large pan of water to a boil and cook the asparagus and beans for 3-4 minutes or until just tender. Drain well and keep warm.
3 Heat the remaining oil in a wide pan. Remove the fish from the marinade then fry skin side down for about 3 minutes then turn over, reduce the heat and cook until the fish is just cooked through. Remove from the pan and keep warm.
4 Add the marinade to the pan and reduce to a syrupy glaze. Serve the fish on the vegetables with the sauce drizzled over.

Per serving: Cals **315** Fat **19.5g** Sat fat **3.5g** Protein **31.8g**

cod with sun-blushed tomato and olive crust

cod with sun-blushed tomato and olive crust

Prep and cook time: 30 mins | Difficulty: easy

Ingredients (for 4 servings)
1 onion, chopped
2 cloves garlic, chopped
150g | ⅓ cup pitted black olives, chopped
12 pieces sun-blushed tomatoes, drained from oil
1tbsp parsley, chopped
1tbsp olive oil
4 medium cod fillets
100ml | 7tbsp dry white wine
Tomatoes on the vine and green beans, to serve

Method
1 Heat the oven to 180ºC/350ºF/Gas Mark 4.
2 Mix together the onion, garlic, olives, sun-blushed tomatoes, parsley and olive oil.
3 Put the fish fillets into a baking dish and pour in the wine.
4 Spread the tomato and olive mixture on the fish fillets and cook for 20 minutes, until the fish flakes easily.
5 Serve with cooked green beans and roasted cherry tomatoes (not included in nutritional values).

Per serving: Cals 245 Fat 8.3g Sat fat 0.5g Protein 24.3g

sea bream with ratatouille

Prep and cook time: 50 mins | Difficulty: medium

Ingredients (for 4 servings)
For the ratatouille:
1tbsp olive oil
2 onions, chopped
4 cloves garlic, chopped
1 aubergine, diced
1 red pepper, deseeded and diced
1 courgette, chopped
4 tomatoes, chopped
2tsp tomato purée
2 sprigs thyme, chopped
Salt and pepper to taste

For the tomato sauce:
1tbsp olive oil
200g | ½lb tomatoes
½tsp sugar
Salt and pepper to taste

For the fish:
1tbsp olive oil
4 sea bream fillets
Juice of 1 lemon

Method
1 Heat 1tbsp oil in a pan and gently cook the onions until translucent.
2 Add the garlic, fry for 1 minute then add the aubergine, pepper and courgette. Gently cook for 4 minutes then add the tomatoes, tomato purée and thyme. Season with salt and pepper and simmer for about 20 minutes, stirring occasionally.
3 Meanwhile, make the sauce. Put the oil, tomatoes and sugar into a blender and whizz until smooth. Push through a fine sieve into a small pan, heat gently and season with salt and pepper.
4 Slash the skin of the fish, rub with the lemon juice and oil and cook, skin-side down, in a hot pan for 4 minutes. Turn and cook until the fish is cooked through.
5 Serve the fish on a bed of sauce and ratatouille.

Per serving: Cals 362 Fat 15.8g Sat fat 2g Protein 34.3g

haddock fillet with poached egg, lentils and spinach

Prep and cook time: 35 mins | Difficulty: easy

Ingredients (for 4 servings)
400g | 2 cups tinned green lentils, drained and rinsed
400g | 2 cups tinned tomatoes, chopped
1tsp curry powder
Salt and pepper to taste
400g | 1lb spinach, washed and stalks removed
4 smoked haddock fillets, dyed or undyed
4 medium eggs

Method
1 Put the lentils into a pan with the tomatoes and curry powder and simmer for 10 minutes. Season with salt and pepper.
2 Add the spinach to the lentils and mix. Place the fish on top of the lentils, cover and cook for about 10 minutes.
3 Fill a wide pan with about 8cm/3in water, and bring it to a boil.
4 Turn the heat down so only a few bubbles rise to the surface. Break the eggs into a cup individually and carefully slip into the water.
5 Poach the eggs for about 3 minutes, then remove from the pan with a slotted spoon and serve with the lentils and fish.

Per serving: Cals **370** Fat **8g** Sat fat **3g** Protein **46g**

polenta with caponata

Prep and cook time: 1 hour | Difficulty: easy

Ingredients (for 4 servings)
180g | 1 cup instant polenta
50g | ½ cup Parmesan cheese, grated
Salt and pepper to taste
1tbsp olive oil
1 onion, sliced
2 cloves garlic, chopped
1 medium aubergine, chopped
1 red pepper, deseeded and chopped
400g | 2 cups cherry tomatoes
2 sprigs fresh thyme, chopped
150g | 2 cups green olives
Basil leaves, to garnish

Method
1 Put 750ml water in a large saucepan, add the polenta and bring to the boil. Cook, stirring all the time, for about 10 minutes or until the mixture comes away from the sides of the pan.
2 Beat in the Parmesan cheese, season with salt and pepper and pour into a 20cm/8in x 20cm/8in baking tin.
3 Heat the oil in a wide non-stick pan, add the onions and cook until translucent; then add the garlic and the aubergine. Cook over a gentle heat for 5 minutes then add the pepper and cook for a further 10 minutes or until the vegetables are tender.
4 Add the tomatoes, thyme and olives, cover the pan and cook for another 10 minutes. Season with salt and pepper and remove from the heat.
5 Cut the polenta into triangles and grill for about 3 minutes on each side in a heated griddle pan.
6 Arrange the polenta on plates, spoon over the caponata and garnish with the basil leaves.

Per serving: Cals **223** Fat **14.8g** Sat fat **2.6g** Protein **7.9g**

haddock fillet with poached egg, lentils and spinach

asian chicken with bean sprouts and red peppers

Prep and cook time: 25 mins | Difficulty: easy

Ingredients (for 4 servings)
1tbsp sesame oil
4 chicken breasts, skinned and sliced into strips
4 spring onions, chopped
2 red peppers, deseeded and cut into strips
200g | 1 cup tinned bamboo shoots
5tbsp soy sauce
1tbsp cornflour
Salt and pepper to taste
50g | ⅓ cup cashew nuts
150g | 1½ cups bean sprouts
2tbsp oyster sauce

Method
1 Heat the oil in a wok or large non-stick pan until smoking, add the chicken and stir-fry for 4 minutes, stirring all the time. Remove the meat and set aside.
2 Add the peppers, spring onions and bamboo shoots and stir-fry for 3 minutes.
3 Mix the soy sauce with the cornflour and a little water and stir into the vegetables.
4 Return the meat to the pan and season.
5 Stir in the cashew nuts and bean sprouts, heat briefly and season to taste with oyster sauce.

Per serving: Cals **280** Fat **12.4g** Sat fat **1.5g** Protein **29g**

asian chicken with bean sprouts and red peppers

oven-baked cod with spinach and pine nuts

Prep and cook time: 50 mins | Difficulty: medium

Ingredients (for 4 servings)
400g | 1lb spinach, washed and stalks removed
Salt and pepper to taste
1tbsp olive oil
3 shallots, chopped
1 stick celery, chopped
250g | 2 cups peeled prawns, chopped
150ml | 2⁄3 cup white wine
150ml | 2⁄3 cup fish stock
6tsp pine nuts
2tbsp chopped basil
2tbsp chopped parsley
4 cod fillets
Juice of 1 lemon

Method:
1 Heat the oven to 200ºC/400ºF/Gas Mark 6.
2 Put the wet spinach in a large pan and cook until the spinach wilts. Drain well, chop and season. Set aside and keep warm.
3 Heat the oil in a non-stick pan and gently cook the shallots until soft. Add the celery and cook for 5 minutes then add the prawns.
4 Pour in the wine, let it reduce by half then add the stock and simmer for 3 minutes.
5 Toast the pine nuts in a dry pan and add to the sauce along with the basil and parsley. Cook for about 2 minutes and season with salt and pepper.
6 Place pieces of fish on aluminium foil. Season with salt, pepper and the lemon juice and seal to make parcels.
7 Bake for about 15 minutes or until the fish flakes easily.
8 Serve the fish on beds of spinach with the sauce poured over.

Per serving: Cals **309** Fat **12.5g** Sat fat **1.2g** Protein **35g**

oven-baked cod with spinach and pine nuts

chicken breast with pea purée

Prep and cook time: 30 mins | Difficulty: medium

Ingredients (for 4 servings)
2tbsp olive oil
Juice of 1 lemon
2tsp honey
Salt and pepper to taste
4 chicken breasts, skinned
800g | 2lb frozen peas
1L | 4 cups chicken stock or water
1tsp sugar
1tbsp mint, chopped
2tbsp shredded basil, to garnish

Method
1 Mix 1 tablespoon of oil, lemon juice and honey, season with salt and
  pepper and rub into the chicken breasts. Set aside while you make
  the purée.
2 Put the peas into the stock, bring to the boil and cook for 3 minutes.
3 Drain the peas, reserving the liquid, then blend with a hand blender to
  make a coarse purée, adding a little of the cooking liquid to achieve
  the right consistency. Add the sugar and mint and season with salt
  and pepper. Set aside and keep warm.
4 Heat the remaining oil in a wide non-stick pan and cook the chicken
  for about 4 minutes on each side or until cooked through.
5 Serve with the pea purée and garnish with the shredded basil.

Per serving: Cals **384** Fat **9g** Sat fat **1g** Protein **39g**

chicken breast with pea purée

mapo doufu (sichuan tofu and pork)

Prep and cook time: 30 mins | Difficulty: easy

Ingredients (for 4 servings)
1tbsp sesame oil
150g | 6oz minced pork
2 cloves garlic, crushed
10 spring onions, sliced
2tbsp chilli bean paste
1tbsp fermented black beans
2tsp powdered Sichuan pepper
250ml | 1 cup chicken stock
400g | 1lb tofu, cubed
2tsp sugar
2tsp light soy sauce
Salt to taste
2tbsp cornflour

Method
1 Heat the oil in a large wok until smoking, then fry the pork until browned all over.
2 Add the garlic and the spring onions and stir-fry for 2 minutes. Stir in the chilli bean paste, black beans and Sichuan pepper and cook for 3 minutes, then gradually add the stock.
3 Bring to the boil, then turn down the heat and add the tofu. Gently simmer for about 5 minutes then stir in the sugar and soy sauce. Season with salt to taste.
4 Mix the cornflour with a little water and stir into the dish. Simmer until thickened and serve with boiled rice (not included in nutritional values).

Per serving: Cals **274** Fat **14.9g** Sat fat **4.4g** Protein **18g**

aubergines with tomatoes and rice

Prep and cook time: 1 hour | Difficulty: easy

Ingredients (for 4 servings)
4 small aubergines
2tbsp olive oil
2 shallots, finely diced
2 cloves garlic, finely chopped
4 spring onions, finely chopped
8 tomatoes, sliced
200g | 1½ cups rice, cooked
2tbsp tomato purée
1tbsp oregano, chopped
Salt and freshly ground pepper to taste
50g | ½ cup Parmesan cheese, grated

Method
1 Heat the oven to 200°C/400°F/Gas Mark 6.
2 Slice the aubergines lengthways and scoop out some of the flesh, leaving a ½cm (¼in) wall. Finely chop the scooped-out flesh.
3 Heat 1 tablespoon of olive oil and cook the aubergine flesh with the shallots and garlic for about 5 minutes, stirring. Add a little water if necessary.
4 Reserve some of the tomato slices and chop the remaining flesh. Mix with the rice, tomato purée and oregano and stir into the aubergine mixture. Season to taste with salt and pepper.
5 Stuff the aubergine halves with the mixture, lay on the reserved tomato slices and sprinkle with cheese.
6 Place the aubergines in an ovenproof dish and bake in the preheated oven for about 30 minutes.
7 Serve with minted yoghurt and flatbread (not included in nutritional information).

Per serving: Cals **401** Fat **11.1g** Sat fat **4.9g** Protein **13.5g**

lentil burgers with yoghurt dip

Prep and cook time: 1 hour 30 mins | Difficulty: medium

Ingredients (for 4 servings)
200g | 1 cup brown lentils
1 sprig thyme
1 bay leaf
50g | 1 cup wholemeal breadcrumbs
1tbsp olive oil
1 onion, finely chopped
2 cloves garlic, finely chopped
5tbsp parsley, finely chopped
1 red chilli pepper, seeds removed, finely chopped
1 carrot, grated
2tbsp sesame seeds
1 pinch ground cumin
1 pinch ground coriander
1 pinch nutmeg
1 pinch cayenne pepper
1 medium egg
2tbsp flour

For the yoghurt dip:
2 spring onions, cut into rings
200ml | ⅞ cup low-fat yoghurt

For the salad:
3 handfuls mixed salad leaves
100g | ½ cup cherry tomatoes, halved
1 cucumber, sliced lengthways with a peeler

Method:
1 Preheat the oven to 220°C/425°F/Gas Mark 7.
2 Rinse lentils. Cook in a lidded pan with 475ml water with the thyme
  sprig and the bay leaf for 35 minutes until soft.
3 Remove the lid and turn up heat. Stir until the liquid has evaporated
  and the lentils begin to disintegrate. Remove thyme and bay leaf.
4 Soften the breadcrumbs in warm water, then squeeze out any excess
  water and add to the lentil mixture.
5 Heat the oil in a non-stick pan and fry the onion and garlic. Add to lentils
  with parsley. Stir in chilli, carrots, sesame, cumin, coriander and nutmeg.
6 Add the egg and flour and mix everything together.
7 Shape into 8 burgers and bake in the oven for 12 minutes or until
  golden brown.
8 To make the yoghurt dip, mix the spring onions with the yoghurt.
9 To make the salad arrange the tomatoes and cucumber on plates.
10 Serve the lentil burgers with the dip and the salad.

Per serving: Cals **265** Fat **8.2g** Sat fat **2.1g** Protein **13.9g**

moroccan chicken skewers

Prep and cook time: 50 mins | Marinade: 3 hours | Difficulty: easy

Ingredients (for 4 servings)
For the chicken skewers:
900g | 2lb chicken breast fillets
2 cloves garlic, finely chopped
Zest and juice of 1 lemon
2tbsp olive oil
Salt and freshly ground pepper to taste
2-3tsp Moroccan spice mixture
12 wooden skewers, soaked

For the yoghurt dip:
250ml | 1 cup low-fat yoghurt
1 pinch Moroccan spice mixture

For the couscous:
50g | 2oz coriander leaves
250g | 1¼ cups couscous
1 lemon, juice only
200g | 7oz ripe tomatoes, chopped
1 onion, finely chopped
1 small aubergine, sliced and grilled
1½ red bell pepper, finely chopped
2tbsp white wine vinegar
Salt and pepper to taste

Method
1 For the chicken skewers: remove any skin or fat from the meat and
  cut into 12 long, thin strips.
2 Mix 2 tablespoons of lemon juice and the olive oil with the garlic, half
  of the lemon zest, salt, pepper and the Moroccan spice mixture.
  Add the chicken, mix well, cover and marinate in the refrigerator for
  about 3 hours.
3 Thread the pieces of meat on wooden skewers. Grill the chicken on
  both sides in a preheated grill.
4 For the dip: mix the yoghurt with the spices until smooth.
5 Cook the couscous according to the packet instructions.
6 Put the lemon juice into a bowl. Chop the aubergine and add with the
  vegetables to the lemon juice in the bowl.
7 Heat a skillet, add the mixed vegetables and sauté briefly. Stir in the
  vinegar and mix the vegetables with the couscous along with the
  coriander. Check the seasoning.
8 Spoon the couscous onto plates or into dishes, add chicken skewers
  and a little yoghurt sauce to each and serve.

Tip: Moroccan spice mixtures usually consist of: paprika (noble sweet),
cumin, turmeric, coriander, cayenne pepper and saffron

Per serving: Cals **319** Fat **10.6g** Sat fat **1.7g** Protein **32.8g**

chicken and vegetable stir-fry

Prep and cook time: 20 mins | Difficulty: easy

Ingredients (for 4 servings)
1tbsp sesame oil
4 chicken breasts, cubed
100g | 1 cup mushrooms, sliced
100g | 4oz asparagus, trimmed and cut into 3cm lengths
100g | 1 cup broccoli florets
1 red chilli, deseeded and sliced
1 shallot, finely sliced
2 cloves garlic, finely sliced
1 carrot, peeled and cut into thin matchsticks
1 small tin baby corn
Thumb-size piece ginger, peeled and grated
1tsp sugar
Light soy sauce, to taste
Fish sauce, to taste

Method
1 Heat the oil in a large wok until smoking.
2 Add the chicken and cook for 1 minute, stirring all the time. Add the
  mushrooms and cook for 1 more minute.
3 Add the asparagus, broccoli, chilli, shallot, garlic, carrot, corn and
  ginger and cook for one minute, stirring all the time, then add a little
  water, turn the heat down and cook for about 3 minutes.
4 Add the sugar and season with soy sauce and fish sauce to taste.

Per serving: Cals **218** Fat **3.8g** Sat fat **0.5g** Protein **27g**

chicken and vegetable stir-fry

fagiolata
(bean soup with pasta)

Prep and cook time: 20 mins | Difficulty: easy

Ingredients (for 4 servings)
1tbsp olive oil
1 onion, chopped
400g | 2 cups tinned tomatoes
1 stalk celery, chopped
1L | 4 cups vegetable stock
200g | 8oz macaroni
400g | 2 cups kidney beans, tinned
20g | 1 cup basil leaves, chopped
20g | 1 cup parsley leaves, chopped
Salt and pepper to taste
2tbsp Parmesan cheese, grated

Method
1 Heat the oil in a pan and sauté the onion until translucent. Add
   the tomatoes and celery, cover and cook over a medium heat for
   about 4-5 minutes.
2 Add the stock and cook over a medium heat for about 30 minutes.
3 Add the macaroni and beans and cook for about 10 more minutes
   until the pasta is done, stirring frequently.
4 Stir in the basil and parsley and season to taste with salt and
   pepper. Serve sprinkled with freshly grated Parmesan.

Per serving: Cals 378 Fat 6.5g Sat fat 1g Protein 15.8g

fagiolata (bean soup with pasta)

warm quinoa salad with red snapper

warm quinoa salad with red snapper

Prep and cook time: 20 mins | Difficulty: easy

Ingredients (for 4 servings)
200g | 1 cup quinoa
2tbsp olive oil
1 red onion, chopped
1 leek, white part only; sliced
2 cloves garlic, chopped
2 courgettes, sliced
4tbsp pine nuts
200ml | ⅞ cup fish stock
12 chives, chopped
3 sprigs dill, chopped
Salt and pepper to taste
400g | 1lb cherry tomatoes
4 fillets red snapper or bream
Dill sprigs, to garnish

Method
1 Cook the quinoa according to the packet instructions. Set aside
  and keep warm.
2 Heat 1 tablespoon of oil in a large non-stick pan and gently cook the
  onion and leek until translucent. Add the garlic, cook for 2 minutes
  then add the courgettes until they soften and just begin to brown.
3 Add the pine nuts and fish stock, bring to a boil then gently stir in
  the quinoa and herbs. Season with salt and pepper, set aside and
  keep warm.
4 Heat a non-stick pan and cook the cherry tomatoes over a high heat
  until they start to blister. Remove and keep warm.
5 Wipe out the pan then add 1 tablespoon of oil. Cook the fish skin-side
  down for 2 minutes then turn, reduce the heat and cook for 3 minutes
  or until the fish is just cooked through.
6 Serve the salad with the snapper and garnish with dill sprigs
  and tomatoes.

Per serving: Cals **543** Fat **18.1g** Sat fat **2.1g** Protein **56.5g**

vegetarian chilli

vegetarian chilli

Prep and cook time: 40 mins | Difficulty: easy

Ingredients (for 4 servings)
1tbsp olive oil
1 large onion, chopped
2 cloves garlic, chopped
4tbsp tomato purée
1tsp chilli powder
500g | 2½ cups tomatoes, chopped
400ml | 1⅔ cups vegetable stock or water
1 red pepper, deseeded and chopped
1 green pepper, deseeded and chopped
2 courgettes, chopped
1 aubergine, chopped
400g | 2 cups tinned red kidney beans, drained and rinsed
1 small tin sweetcorn, drained and rinsed
Parsley, to garnish

Method
1 Heat the oil in a large pan and gently cook the onions until
   translucent. Add the garlic, cook for 1 minute then stir in the chilli
   powder and the tomato purée.
2 Add half the tomatoes and blend to a purée with a hand blender.
3 Pour in the stock or water then add the vegetables and the remaining
   tomatoes. Simmer gently for about 20 minutes or until all the
   vegetables are tender.
4 Season with salt and pepper and serve with boiled rice (not included
   in nutritional values), garnishing with parsley.

Per serving: Cals **279** Fat **6.6g** Sat fat **0.5g** Protein **15.4g**

chicken with courgettes and spinach on rice

Prep and cook time: 30 mins | Difficulty: easy

Ingredients (for 4 servings)
300g | 1½ cups brown basmati rice
1tbsp sesame oil
2 chicken breasts, cut into strips
150g | 6oz tofu, sliced
2 courgettes, sliced thinly lengthwise
150g | 2 cups button mushrooms, thinly sliced
2 handfuls baby spinach
2tbsp light soy sauce

Method
1 Cook the basmati rice according to the packet instructions.
2 Heat the oil in a wok or frying pan until smoking and stir-fry the strips
   of chicken breasts for 2 minutes.
3 Add the tofu, courgettes and mushrooms and cook for 3 minutes or
   until the vegetables are just tender.
4 Add the baby spinach and cook until it wilts then splash in the
   soy sauce.
5 Spoon the rice on to plates and arrange the chicken, tofu, courgettes,
   mushrooms and spinach on top.

Per serving: Cals **422** Fat **9.2g** Sat fat **1.4g** Protein **27.4g**

chicken with lime and mint on rice noodles

chicken with lime and mint
on rice noodles

Prep and cook time: 30 mins | Marinade: 30 mins | Difficulty: easy

Ingredients (for 4 servings)
6tbsp lime juice
1tbsp fish sauce
2tsp sugar
4 chicken breasts, skinned
300g | ¾lb rice noodles
1 red chilli, deseeded and chopped
1 carrot
1 small courgette
20g | 1 cup fresh mint leaves
3tbsp olive oil
Lime zest, to garnish

Method
1 Mix 3 tablespoons of the lime juice, the fish sauce and sugar and rub
  into the chicken breasts. Leave to marinate for about 30 minutes,
  turning from time to time.
2 Cook the noodles in plenty of boiling, salted water until al dente, then
  drain through a strainer and rinse thoroughly.
3 Peel the carrot, wash the courgette and cut both lengthwise into thin
  ribbons, using a mandolin vegetable slicer if available. Strip the leaves
  off the mint stalks.
4 Mix 1 tablespoon of oil with the remaining lime juice and mix into the
  noodles, carrots, courgette and mint leaves and serve into bowls.
5 Take the chicken out of the marinade, heat the remaining oil in a frying
  pan and fry the chicken for about 5 minutes each side.
6 Slice the chicken breasts across thickly and arrange on the noodles.
  Sprinkle with the chopped chilli and garnish with lime zest.

Per serving: Cals **323** Fat **12.6g** Sat fat **1.5g** Protein **25.3g**

pappardelle with white beans and tuna

Prep and cook time: 30 mins | Difficulty: easy

Ingredients (for 4 servings)
400g | 1lb pappardelle
1tbsp olive oil
1 onion, finely chopped
2 cloves garlic, chopped
400g | 2 cups tinned tomatoes, chopped
400g | 2 cups tinned haricot beans, drained and rinsed
Chilli flakes
350g | 2 tins tuna, drained
Salt and pepper to taste
Oregano leaves, to garnish

Method
1 Bring a large pan of salted water to a boil and cook the pappardelle until al dente.
2 Meanwhile, heat the oil in a pan. Cook the onions until translucent then add the garlic and cook for 2 minutes.
3 Add the tomatoes, beans and chilli flakes. Simmer for about 10 minutes, then add the tuna and season to taste.
4 Drain the pasta, adding a few tablespoonfuls of the pasta water to the sauce. Toss the pasta in the sauce, then arrange on pre-warmed plates and serve. Garnish with oregano or other fresh herbs.

Per serving: Cals **474** Fat **6.9g** Sat fat **0.5g** Protein **39g**

turkey and mushroom casserole with tomatoes and pumpkin seeds

Prep and cook time: 1 hour 25 mins | Difficulty: easy

Ingredients (for 4 servings)
2tbsp plain flour
Salt and pepper to taste
500g | 1lb turkey steaks, cubed
2 rashers bacon, rind removed, cut into strips
250g | 9oz button mushrooms
750ml | 3 cups dry white wine
600ml | 2½ cups chicken stock
2 cloves garlic, chopped
250g | 9oz tomatoes, thickly sliced
2tbsp pumpkin seeds

Method
1 Put the flour, salt and pepper into a large plastic food bag. Add the turkey to the bag and shake to coat evenly.
2 Put the bacon into a large non-stick pan over a low heat. Fry until the fat melts in the pan, stirring frequently, then remove it and set aside.
3 Add the turkey over a medium heat for 2-3 minutes until lightly browned all over. Then add the carrots, celery and mushrooms for about 5 minutes, or until softened and lightly browned. Remove and set aside.
4 Increase the heat, add the wine and scrape up the sticky juices. Boil the mixture until it has reduced by half, then add the stock, return to the boil and cook until it has reduced by a third.
5 Return the bacon, turkey and vegetables to the pan with the garlic and tomatoes. Reduce the heat and simmer, uncovered, for 20-30 minutes until the turkey is tender.
6 Transfer to a serving dish and scatter with the pumpkin seeds.

Per serving: Cals **406** Fat **6.4g** Sat fat **0.7g** Protein **39.7g**

pappardelle with white beans and tuna

seared tuna with broad beans and serrano ham

seared tuna with broad beans and serrano ham

Prep and cook time: 40 mins | Difficulty: easy

Ingredients (for 4 servings)
300g | 4 cups podded broad beans
2tbsp olive oil
1 clove garlic, finely sliced
Salt and pepper to taste
4 slices serrano ham, chopped
4 fresh tuna steaks
1tbsp cracked black pepper
Parsley, to garnish

Method:
1 Boil the broad beans in salted water for 5 minutes or until tender.
2 Drain well and slip the beans from their skins by squeezing gently between your fingers.
3 Heat 1 tablespoon of oil in a non-stick pan and gently fry the garlic until it is soft but not coloured. Add the serrano ham and cook for 2 more minutes. Stir in the broad beans, season with salt and pepper and remove the pan from the heat.
4 Add the cracked black pepper to the tuna steaks. Heat 1 tablespoon of oil in a pan until very hot and cook the tuna for about 2 minutes on each side, or to your liking.
5 Reheat the broad beans and ham and serve with the tuna. Garnish with parsley.

Per serving: Cals **501** Fat **21g** Sat fat **5g** Protein **59g**

beef and barley soup

Prep and cook time: 1 hour 45 mins | Difficulty: easy

Ingredients (for 4 servings)
1 piece stewing beef, approx 400g/1lb
1 bay leaf
6 crushed allspice berries
200g | 1 cup pearl barley
2 potatoes, diced
2 carrots, chopped
2 sticks celery, chopped
2 onions, chopped
1 sprig rosemary, chopped
1 sprig thyme, chopped
2 sprigs parsley, chopped
Salt and pepper to taste

Method

1 Wash and dry the meat. Put into a pan with about 1 litre water (the meat should be covered) and bring to the boil. Turn the heat down to a simmer and add the bay leaf and allspice berries.

2 After about half an hour rinse the pearl barley under running water and add to the meat. Cook for 10 minutes then add the vegetables and herbs.

3 Cook for another 20 minutes or until the vegetables are tender. Add more water if necessary during cooking. Take the meat out, cut into small pieces and return to the pan.

4 Season to taste with salt and pepper and serve.

Per serving: Cals **558** Fat **16g** Sat fat **6g** Protein **31.5g**

risotto with chicken and mushrooms

Prep and cook time: 40 mins | Difficulty: medium

Ingredients (for 4 servings)
2tbsp olive oil
4 shallots, finely chopped
300g | 1½ cups Arborio rice
100ml | 7tbsp white wine
Approx 1L | 4 cups chicken stock, hot
4 chicken breasts, skinned
200g | 2 cups mushrooms, sliced
4 spring onions, sliced
50g | ½ cup Parmesan cheese, grated
Salt and pepper to taste

Method

1 Heat the olive oil in a wide non-stick pan and gently fry the shallots until translucent. Add the rice and stir for 3 minutes until all the rice is coated with the oil.

2 Add the white wine, cook for 1 minute then gradually add the stock, stirring all the time. Continue until the rice is nearly cooked then take off the heat and keep warm.

3 Cut the chicken into strips and fry gently in a non-stick frying pan until lightly browned. Remove from the pan and keep warm.

4 Add the mushrooms to the pan and cook until tender.

5 Stir the chicken, mushrooms, spring onions and Parmesan into the rice, season with salt and pepper and serve immediately.

Per serving: Cals **659** Fat **12.6g** Sat fat **3.1g** Protein **53.5g**

risotto with chicken and mushrooms

chicken with moroccan spices, pumpkin and tomatoes

chicken with moroccan spices, pumpkin and tomatoes

Prep and cook time: 1 hour | Difficulty: easy

Ingredients (for 4 servings)
4 chicken breasts, with skin
4 cloves garlic
30g fresh coriander
½tsp sweet paprika
½tsp cumin
½tsp turmeric
1tbsp olive oil
2tbsp lemon juice
Salt and pepper to taste
400g | 1lb butternut squash, peeled and deseeded
400g | 1lb cherry tomatoes, on the vine

Method:

1 Preheat the oven to 175ºC/350ºF/Gas Mark 4.

2 Peel and roughly chop the garlic. Put into a mortar with the coriander (reserve a few leaves to garnish), paprika, cumin, turmeric, olive oil and the lemon juice and crush to a fine paste.

3 Season the paste then rub into the chicken breasts.

4 Cut the pumpkin into wedges and put into a baking dish with the washed and drained tomatoes. Season with salt and pepper.

5 Place the chicken breasts on top of the vegetables, skin side up, and cook in the preheated oven for about 30 minutes.

6 Serve scattered with the reserved coriander leaves.

Per serving: Cals **480** Fat **19.7g** Sat fat **4.5g** Protein **59.9g**

quinoa with butternut squash, kale and roasted garlic

Prep and cook time: 40 mins | Difficulty: easy

Ingredients (for 4 servings)
4 heads garlic
1tbsp olive oil
2 onions, sliced
800g | 2lb butternut squash or pumpkin, peeled, seeds removed and cubed
300g | 1½ cups quinoa, soaked for 10 minutes
600ml | 2½ cups chicken stock or water
400g | 1lb curly kale or green cabbage, chopped
Salt and pepper to taste
Thyme and parsley, to garnish

Method

1 Heat the oven to 200ºC/400ºF/Gas Mark 6.

2 Wrap each garlic head in tinfoil, bake in the oven for about 30 minutes or until tender.

3 Meanwhile, heat the olive oil in a wide pan and gently fry the onions for 10 minutes. Stir in the squash or pumpkin, quinoa and chicken stock. Bring to a boil then turn the heat down and simmer for 10-15 minutes or until the squash is nearly tender.

4 Add the kale and a little more water if necessary, cover and cook for 3 minutes. Season with salt and pepper.

5 Cut the tops off the baked garlic and serve alongside the quinoa and squash. Garnish with the herbs.

Per serving: Cals **300** Fat **7.5g** Sat fat **0.5g** Protein **13.8g**

lentil curry with mangetout and tofu

Prep and cook time: 20 mins | Difficulty: easy

Ingredients (for 4 servings)
1tbsp olive oil
1 onion, sliced
1 clove garlic, crushed
1tbsp curry power
2 carrots, cut into batons
200g | 8oz tofu, cubed
250ml | 1 cup chicken stock or water
200g mangetout, halved diagonally
2 tins green lentils, drained and rinsed
Parsley, to garnish

Method
1 Heat the oil in a non-stick pan and cook the onion until translucent.
2 Add the garlic and curry powder and cook for 2 minutes, stirring all the time.
3 Add the carrots, tofu and the stock, bring to a boil and cook for 3 minutes. Add the mangetout and cook until tender, adding a little more water if necessary.
4 Stir through the lentils for 5 minutes, till warmed through, then serve with parsley to garnish.

Per serving: Cals 254 Fat 6.5g Sat fat 1g Protein 19g

lentil curry with mangetout and tofu

turkey burgers with honey and mustard dressing

Prep and cook time: 20 mins | Difficulty: easy

Ingredients (for 4 servings)
400g | 1lb turkey mince
Salt and pepper to taste
1tbsp wholegrain mustard
2tsp honey
1tsp lemon juice
1tbsp olive oil

To serve:
4 burger buns
Lettuce
Tomato, sliced
Red onion, sliced

Method
1 Season the turkey mince with salt and pepper and mix well with your hands. Shape into 4 burgers.
2 In a small bowl, mix the honey, mustard and lemon juice and season to taste.
3 Heat the oil in a wide non-stick frying pan and cook the burgers for about 5 minutes on each side or until cooked through.
4 Serve the buns with the honey and mustard dressing, lettuce and tomato and onion to garnish.

Per serving: Cals **364** Fat **15g** Sat fat **3.5g** Protein **27.5g**

stir-fried prawns with tofu

Prep and cook time: 20 mins | Difficulty: easy

Ingredients (for 4 servings)
1tbsp sesame oil
2 cloves garlic
1 green chilli, deseeded and chopped
Thumb-size piece fresh ginger, peeled and finely sliced
200g | 8oz tofu, cubed
4 runner beans, very thinly sliced
400g | 1lb tiger prawns, tails on
200ml | ⅞ cup fish stock
2tsp fish sauce
Pinch sugar

Method
1 Heat the oil in a large wok until smoking. Add the garlic, chilli and ginger and stir-fry for 2 minutes.
2 Add the tofu and the beans, cook for 2 minutes then add the prawns. Cook for 30 seconds then add the stock, fish sauce and sugar.
3 Bring to a boil, bubble for 2 minutes and serve immediately.

Per serving: Cals **129** Fat **6.9g** Sat fat **1g** Protein **15g**

stir-fried prawns with tofu

asian noodles with tofu and peppers

Prep and cook time: 20 mins | Difficulty: easy

Ingredients (for 4 servings)
200g | 8oz egg noodles
200g | 8oz tofu, cubed
2tbsp sesame oil
3tbsp soy sauce
3 spring onions, chopped
2 cloves garlic, chopped
Thumb-sized piece fresh ginger, peeled and grated
100g | 1 cup mushrooms, sliced
1 red pepper, deseeded and chopped
1 yellow pepper, deseeded and chopped
1tbsp rice wine or dry sherry
2tbsp parsley, chopped

Method

1 Cook the noodles according to the packet instructions, Drain, rinse under running water and set aside.
2 Mix the tofu with 1 tablespoon of soy sauce and 1 tablespoon of sesame oil and set aside.
3 Heat 1 tablespoon of oil in a wok until smoking and toss the noodles until coated with oil. Remove from the wok and set aside.
4 Add the spring onion, garlic and ginger, stir-fry for 1 minute then add the tofu, mushrooms and peppers.
5 Continue cooking, stirring all the time, until the vegetables are just cooked. Add the parsley, the rest of the soy sauce and rice wine then stir in the noodles to heat through. Serve immediately.

Per serving: Cals 207 Fat **7.2g** Sat fat **1.5g** Protein **8g**

stuffed peppers with tomato sauce

Prep and cook time: 1 hour | Difficulty: easy

Ingredients (for 4 servings)
For the tomato sauce:
1tbsp olive oil
1 onion, finely chopped
2 cloves garlic, chopped
400g | 2 cups tinned tomatoes
250ml | 1 cup chicken stock
1tsp dried oregano
Salt and pepper to taste

For the stuffed peppers:
1tbsp olive oil
1 onion, finely chopped
2 cloves garlic, chopped
3 slices bacon, chopped
150g | 3 cups fresh breadcrumbs
1tbsp capers, chopped
25g | 1 cup parsley, coarsely chopped
8 medium red peppers

Method

1 To make the sauce, heat the oil in a non-stick pan and gently cook the onion until translucent. Add the garlic and cook for 2 more minutes then add the tomatoes, chicken stock and oregano.
2 Simmer gently for 25 minutes, stirring occasionally, and season with salt and pepper.
3 Meanwhile, heat the oven to 180ºC/375ºF/Gas Mark 5.
4 For the stuffed peppers, heat the oil in a wide non-stick pan and gently cook the onion until translucent. Add the garlic and bacon and cook for a further 5 minutes.
5 Turn up the heat then add the breadcrumbs and cook until they are lightly browned and crisp. Stir in the capers and parsley and season with salt and pepper.
6 Cut the tops off the peppers and carefully remove the seeds. Stuff the peppers with the breadcrumb mixture, replace the lids and put them in a deep ovenproof dish.
7 Pour the tomato sauce around the peppers and bake for about 20 minutes or until the peppers are tender.

Per serving: Cals 299 Fat **9.5g** Sat fat **2.1g** Protein **10.6g**

asian noodles with tofu and peppers

spaghetti with vegetables and mushrooms

Prep and cook time: 45 mins | **Difficulty: easy**

Ingredients (for 4 servings)
400g | 1lb spaghetti
1tbsp olive oil
1 onion, chopped
2 cloves garlic, chopped
1 carrot, peeled and cut into batons
1 red pepper, deseeded and cut into strips
1 green pepper, deseeded and cut into strips
225g | 8oz mushrooms, sliced
Juice of 1 lemon
125ml | ½ cup vegetable stock or water
25g | ¼ cup grated Parmesan cheese
Basil leaves, to garnish

Method

1 Bring a large pan of salted water to a boil and cook the spaghetti
   until al dente.
2 Meanwhile, heat the oil in a wide non-stick pan and fry the onion and
   the garlic until soft. Add the carrot and peppers and cook for a further
   5 minutes.
3 Add the mushrooms to the other vegetables and stir in the lemon
   juice. Pour in the vegetable stock, simmer for 2 minutes and season
   with salt and pepper.
4 Drain the spaghetti, then carefully stir in with the vegetables and place
   on warmed plates. Sprinkle freshly grated Parmesan cheese over the
   top, garnish with basil and serve.

Per serving: Cals **544** Fat **8g** Sat fat **1.5g** Protein **19.3g**

lamb kebabs with courgettes and tomato sauce

Prep and cook time: 30 mins | **Marinade:** 1 hour | **Difficulty: easy**

Ingredients (for 4 servings)
For the kebabs:
400g | 1lb lamb, from the leg, boned, trimmed and cut into
bite-sized pieces
1tbsp sesame oil
2tbsp dry sherry
1 clove garlic, crushed
1 piece fresh ginger, 3 cm/1in, grated
1tsp honey
1 courgette, thickly sliced
Wooden skewers, soaked in water
Salt to taste

For the tomato sauce:
1tbsp olive oil
1 shallot, peeled and finely diced
1 clove garlic, peeled and finely diced
6 tomatoes, diced
50ml | 10tsp white wine
1tbsp thyme, chopped
Cayenne pepper

Method

1 Mix the sesame oil, sherry, garlic, ginger and honey and marinate the
   lamb in the mixture for about 1 hour.
2 For the sauce, heat the olive oil in a pan and cook the garlic and
   shallot until soft. Add the tomatoes and white wine and simmer for
   5-10 minutes. Then add the thyme and season to taste with salt and
   cayenne pepper.
3 Thread the lamb and courgettes on wooden skewers, brush with the
   remaining marinade and grill for 6-8 minutes, turning occasionally.
4 Season and serve with the tomato sauce.

Per serving: Cals **324** Fat **14.1g** Sat fat **4g** Protein **30g**

rigatoni with spinach and cherry tomatoes

Prep and cook time: 30 mins | Difficulty: easy

Ingredients (for 4 servings)
300g | 12oz rigatoni
400g | 1lb spinach, stalks removed
1tbsp olive oil
1 onion, chopped
1 clove garlic, chopped
200g | 1 cup cherry tomatoes, halved
25g | ¼ cup Parmesan cheese, grated

Method
1 Bring a large pan of salted water to a boil and cook the rigatoni until al dente.
2 Meanwhile, wash the spinach and blanch briefly in boiling, salted water. Refresh in cold water, squeeze out and chop roughly.
3 Heat the oil in a non-stick frying pan and gently cook the onion until translucent. Add the garlic and cook for 1 minute, then add the tomatoes and spinach and cook for 1-2 minutes.
4 Stir in the drained pasta and a little of the pasta water and toss to mix with the vegetables.
5 Season to taste with salt and pepper and serve sprinkled with the Parmesan.

Per serving: Cals **402** Fat **5g** Sat fat **0.5g** Protein **14.3g**

spaghetti napoli

Prep and cook time: 30 mins | Difficulty: easy

Ingredients (for 4 servings)
400g | 1lb spaghetti
1tbsp olive oil
1 onion, chopped
2 cloves garlic, chopped
1 stick celery, chopped
100ml | 7tbsp red wine
400g | 2 cups tinned tomatoes, chopped
100g | 1 cup black olives
½tsp sugar
Salt and pepper to taste
2tbsp chopped basil

Method
1 Bring a large pan of salted water to a boil and cook the spaghetti according to the packet instructions.
2 Meanwhile, heat the oil in a non-stick pan and gently cook the onions until soft. Add the garlic, cook for 1 minute then add the celery. Cook for 5 minutes then add the wine.
3 Allow the wine to bubble for 1 minute, then add the tomatoes and cook for about 15 minutes, stirring occasionally. Stir in the olives and the sugar and season with salt and pepper.
4 Stir the sauce into the drained spaghetti and serve garnished with the basil.

Per serving: Cals **523** Fat **8g** Sat fat **0.5g** Protein **15.3g**

lentil shepherd's pie

Prep and cook time: 1 hour 30 mins | Difficulty: easy

Ingredients (for 4 portions, 4 ramekins)
300g | ¾lb floury potatoes
1tbsp olive oil
1 onion, finely chopped
1 carrot, finely chopped
1 red pepper, deseeded and chopped
1tbsp plain flour
250ml | 1 cup vegetable stock or water
100g | 1 cup peas, frozen
200g | 1 cup green lentils, canned, rinsed and drained
Salt and pepper to taste
75ml | ⅓ cup hot semi-skimmed milk
Nutmeg
50g | ½ cup Cheddar cheese, grated

Method

1 Heat the oven to 200°C/400°F/Gas Mark 6.
2 Cook the potatoes in boiling salted water for around 25 minutes until soft.
3 Heat the oil in a non-stick pan and cook the onions for 5 minutes then add the carrot and pepper and cook until the vegetables are tender.
4 Dust with the flour and add the vegetable stock. Bring to the boil, stir in the peas and lentils and season with salt and pepper.
5 Drain and mash the potatoes, stir in the hot milk and season with salt, pepper and nutmeg to taste.
6 Spoon the lentil mixture into 4 lightly greased ramekins, top with mashed potato and scatter with cheese.
7 Bake in the middle of the oven for 30 minutes until golden brown.

Per serving: Cals **271** Fat **9g** Sat fat **3.9g** Protein **13.3g**

penne with pumpkin

Prep and cook time: 30 mins | Difficulty: easy

Ingredients (for 4 servings)
400g | 1lb penne
1tbsp olive oil
2 red onions, sliced
2 cloves garlic, crushed
400g | 2 cups butternut squash, peeled, deseeded and cubed
100ml | 7tbsp white wine
25g | 1 cup basil, finely shredded
Pinch chilli flakes
25g | ¼ cup Parmesan cheese, grated

Method:

1 Bring a large pan of salted water to a boil and cook the penne until al dente.
2 Meanwhile, heat the oil in a wide non-stick frying pan and gently fry the onions until translucent. Add the garlic, cook for 2 minutes then stir in the squash.
3 Add the white wine and simmer gently until the squash is just tender, adding a little water if necessary.
4 Add the basil then stir the mixture through the cooked pasta. Season to taste and add the chilli flakes. Sprinkle Parmesan over the top and serve.

Per serving: Cals **510** Fat **5.8g** Sat fat **0.5g** Protein **12.6g**

lentil shepherd's pie

mixed braised vegetables with coriander leaves

Prep and cook time: 30 mins | Difficulty: easy

Ingredients (for 4 servings)
1tbsp olive oil
2 large red onions, peeled and cut into wedges
400g | 1lb pearl onions, peeled
1tbsp sugar
400g | 1lb pumpkin, skinned, deseeded and diced
3 red peppers, deseeded and chopped
2tsp dried oregano
100ml | 7tbsp vegetable stock
Salt and pepper to taste
2 sprigs coriander, to garnish

Method
1 Heat the oil in a large non-stick pan with a lid, cook the red onions for 5 minutes then add the pearl onions.
2 Stir in the sugar, cover and cook over a high heat for 2 minutes then add the pumpkin and reduce the heat.
3 Stir carefully then add the red peppers and oregano. Cook for 5 minutes then add the vegetable stock and simmer for 10 minutes. Season with salt and pepper.
4 Garnish with the coriander leaves.

Per serving: Cals **162** Fat **3.6g** Sat fat **0.5g** Protein **3.5g**

mixed braised vegetables with coriander leaves

snacks

houmous

Prep and cook time: 15 mins | Difficulty: easy

Ingredients (for 4 servings)
400g | 2 cups tinned chickpeas, drained and rinsed
3 cloves garlic, chopped
2tbsp tahini paste
Juice of 2 lemons
½tsp ground cumin
Approx 3tbsp olive oil
Salt and ground black pepper to taste

To serve:
1tsp paprika
4 pitta breads, toasted

Method
1 Put the chickpeas into a food processor. Add the garlic, tahini paste,
lemon juice, oil and cumin and process until smooth. Add a little water
if the mixture is too firm. Season with salt and ground black pepper.
2 Serve sprinkled with paprika alongside the pitta breads.

Per serving: Cals 348 Fat 16.4g Sat fat 2g Protein 4.5g

two rice cakes with low-fat soft cheese

Per serving (using 2tbsp low-fat soft cheese): Cals 140 Fat 6g
Sat fat 4g Protein 6g

watermelon

Per 150g | 1 cup serving: Cals 46 Fat 0g Sat fat 0g Protein 1g

granola bars

Prep and cook time: 30 mins | Difficulty: easy

Ingredients (for 16 squares)
100g | ½ cup butter
4tbsp molasses
2½tbsp dark brown sugar
100g | 1 cup rolled oats
2tbsp sunflower seeds
1½tbsp pumpkin seeds
1½tbsp sesame seeds
150g | 1 cup dried apricots, chopped

Method
1 Heat the oven to 175ºC/350ºF/Gas Mark 4.
2 Put the butter, molasses and sugar in a pan and heat until the
butter has melted and the sugar has dissolved.
3 Stir into the remaining ingredients and pour into a non-stick
20cm/8in x 20cm/8in tin and bake for 20 minutes.
4 Leave to cool and cut into squares.

Per serving: Cals 100 Fat 4.6g Sat fat 2g Protein 2.1g

houmous

cranberry and fig flapjacks

Prep and cook time: 1 hour | **Difficulty:** easy

Ingredients (For 16 squares)
175g | ¾ cup unsalted butter
175g soft brown sugar
4tbsp golden syrup
Zest of 1 orange
325g | 3 cups rolled oats
150g | 1 cup dried figs, chopped
150g | 1 cup dried cranberries

Method

1 Heat the oven to 180ºC/350ºF/Gas Mark 4.
2 Melt the butter in a large pan and stir in the sugar and golden syrup.
  Cook over a gentle heat until the sugar has dissolved.
3 Remove from the heat and stir in the orange zest, oats, figs
  and cranberries.
4 Pour into a non-stick 20cm/8in x 20cm/8in baking tray and bake for
  about 40 minutes.
5 Leave in the tin until cooled then cut into squares.

Per serving: Cals **269** Fat **10.2g** Sat fat **5.7g** Protein **2.7g**

handful of brazil nuts

Per serving: Cals **171** Fat **17g** Sat fat **4g** Protein **4g**

white bean purée with olive oil and thyme

Prep and cook time: 1 hour | **Difficulty:** easy

Ingredients (for 4 servings)
2tbsp olive oil
1 onion, chopped
2 cloves garlic
400g | 2 cups haricot beans, soaked overnight
500ml | 2 cups chicken stock or water
4 sprigs thyme
2tbsp low-fat crème fraîche
Salt and pepper to taste
Fresh oregano, to garnish

Method

1 Heat 1 tablespoon of oil in a large pan and cook the onion and garlic
  until translucent.
2 Drain the beans, rinse and add to the pan with the stock and thyme.
3 Bring to a boil and cook until the beans are soft, stirring occasionally.
4 Drain the beans, reserving the cooking broth.
5 Remove the thyme sprigs from the beans and purée the mixture in a
  blender until smooth.
6 Stir in the crème fraîche, remaining oil and enough broth to form a
  creamy purée.
7 Season to taste and garnish with sprigs of fresh oregano.

Per serving: Cals **130** Fat **8.5g** Sat fat **0.5g** Protein **25g**

two rice cakes with peanut butter

Per serving (using 2tbsp peanut butter): Cals **258** Fat **16g** Sat fat **2.6g**
Protein **7.7g**

cranberry and fig flapjacks

fruit loaf

Prep and cook time: 1 hour 50 mins | **Soaking:** 4 hours
Difficulty: easy

Ingredients (for 1 loaf)
450g | 1lb mixed dried fruit
50g | ⅔ cup flaked almonds
225g | 1 cup brown sugar
Warm tea
2tbsp marmalade
1tsp ground cinnamon
1 medium egg
450g | 1lb flour

Method
1 Put the fruit, almonds and sugar into a bowl and cover with warm tea. Cover bowl and leave to soak for at least 4 hours or overnight.
2 Heat the oven to 170°C/325°F/Gas Mark 3. Grease a 1kg/2lb loaf tin.
3 Stir the marmalade, cinnamon, egg and flour into the soaked fruit and beat well until thoroughly combined. Spoon into the tin and bake for about 90 minutes until cooked through.
4 Leave in the tin for 15 minutes before turning out onto a wire rack to cool. Slice into 12 servings.

Per serving: Cals **310** Fat **2.7g** Sat fat **0.3g** Protein **4.9g**

a handful of mixed olives

Per serving: Cals **212** Fat **21g** Sat fat **3g** Protein **2g**

three scottish oatcakes with low-fat cream cheese

Per serving (using 2tbsp of low-fat soft cheese): Cals **205** Fat **11.7g** Sat fat **7g** Protein **7.6g**

two crispbreads with cottage cheese and radishes

Per serving (using 2tbsp cottage cheese): Cals **121** Fat **2.4g** Sat fat **1g** Protein **6.4g**

a banana

Per serving (medium size): Cals **90** Fat **0g** Sat fat **0g** Protein **1g**

an orange

Per serving (medium size): Cals **62** Fat **0g** Sat fat **0g** Protein **1g**

an apple

Per serving (medium size): Cals **72** Fat **0g** Sat fat **0g** Protein **0g**

sweets

vanilla yoghurt with amaranth seeds and strawberries

Prep and cook time: 20 mins | Difficulty: easy

Ingredients (for 4 servings)
4tbsp | ¼ cup amaranth seeds
400g | 2 cups strawberries
½tsp vanilla extract
750g | 3 cups low-fat Greek yoghurt
1tbsp honey

Method
1 Heat a dry frying pan and toast the amaranth seeds, shaking the pan all the time, for about 1 minute. Set aside to cool.
2 Set aside 4 whole strawberries. Slice the remainder, and set half of the strawberry slices around the bottom of 4 serving glasses.
3 Mix the vanilla extract with the yoghurt and honey then stir in the amaranth seeds, reserving 1 tablespoon for garnish.
4 Carefully spoon some of the yoghurt into each glass, add the chopped strawberries and top with the remaining yoghurt.
5 Garnish with the remaining amaranth seeds and the whole strawberries.

Per serving: Cals **171** Fat **2.9g** Sat fat **0g** Protein **24.5g**

apple compote with vanilla yoghurt

Prep and cook time: 30 mins | Difficulty: easy

Ingredients (for 4 servings)
4 cooking apples, peeled, cored and chopped
Juice of 1 lemon
2tbsp brown sugar
1 vanilla pod, cut in half
200g | ¾ cup low-fat yoghurt
½tsp vanilla extract

Method
1 Put the apples into a pan with the lemon juice, sugar and the vanilla pod. Cover and bring to the boil, then simmer for 5 minutes or until the apples are tender.
2 Mix together the yoghurt and the vanilla extract.
3 Spoon the apple compote into glasses and add a layer of vanilla yoghurt to serve.

Per serving: Cals **176** Fat **1g** Sat fat **0.5g** Protein **3g**

baked peaches

Prep and cook time: 15 mins | Difficulty: easy

Ingredients (for 4 servings)
8 ripe peaches, halved, stones removed
50g | ¼ cup caster sugar
Juice of 1 orange
2tbsp dark rum
2tbsp maple syrup

Method
1 Heat the oven with grill to medium temperature.
2 Bring a large pan of water to a boil and blanch the peaches
  for 3 minutes. Drain and pat dry.
3 Put the caster sugar into a saucepan and heat until a caramel is
  formed. Add the peaches, orange juice, rum and maple syrup and
  simmer for 2 minutes.
4 Put the peaches in an ovenproof dish and bake for 5 minutes.
5 Serve the peaches with low-fat frozen yoghurt (not included in
  nutritional values).

Per serving: Cals **222** Fat **2g** Sat fat **0g** Protein **2g**

quinoa with peaches and almonds

Prep and cook time: 20 mins | Difficulty: easy

Ingredients (for 4 servings)
300g | 1½ cups quinoa
400ml | 1⅔ cups water
300ml | 1⅓ cups apple juice
40g | ½ cup flaked almonds
2 ripe peaches
2tbsp peach jam
12 whole almonds

Method
1 Put the quinoa into a pan with the water and apple juice. Bring to
  the boil and cook for about 15 minutes, stirring frequently.
2 Stir in the flaked almonds and divide the mixture between 4 bowls.
3 Cut the peaches in half, remove the stones and cut into wedges.
4 Drizzle over the peach jam and scatter over the whole almonds.

Per serving: Cals **286** Fat **8.9g** Sat fat **0.5g** Protein **6.5g**

açai berry mousse

Prep and cook time: 30 mins | Set: 2 hours | Difficulty: medium

Ingredients (for 4 servings)
4 leaves gelatine
750ml | 3 cups açai juice
4tbsp sugar
Juice of ½ lemon
150ml | ⅔ cup whipping cream
2 medium egg whites

Method
1 Soak the gelatine in a little of the açai juice for 10 minutes, then put
  into a small pan and heat until the gelatine has melted.
2 Add the rest of the juice, the sugar and lemon juice and let cool.
3 Whip the cream and fold into the juice mixture.
4 Whisk the egg whites until they form soft peaks and fold into the mix.
  Pour into a bowl or 4 individual bowls and chill for two hours until set.
5 Serve the mousse sprinkled with muesli and chopped banana (not
  included in nutritional values).

Per serving: Cals **249** Fat **7.9g** Sat fat **5.2g** Protein **9.6g**

baked peaches

baked apples with raisins, pistachios and almonds

Prep and cook time: 45 mins | Difficulty: easy

Ingredients (for 4 servings)
4 large cooking apples
50g | ⅓ cup raisins
3tbsp flaked almonds
2tbsp pistachios
2tbsp honey
1tsp cinnamon

Method
1 Heat the oven to 200°C/400°F/Gas Mark 6. Remove the apple cores with a potato peeler, then carefully scoop out some of the flesh with a pointed spoon.
2 Chop the flesh removed from the apples and mix with the raisins, almonds, pistachios, honey and cinnamon.
3 Put the apples in a baking dish and stuff with the mixture, spooning any excess around the base of the apples, then bake for about 30 minutes. Serve with low-fat Greek yoghurt (not included in nutritional values).

Per serving: Cals **269** Fat **8g** Sat fat **0.8g** Protein **1.8g**

raspberry champagne sorbet

Prep and cook time: 30 mins | Freezing: 6 hours | Difficulty: easy

Ingredients (for 4 servings)
200g | 1 cup sugar
250g | 2 cups raspberries
Juice of ½ lemon
500ml | 2 cups Champagne or sparkling wine

Method
1 Put the sugar in a pan with 200ml water. Bring to the boil and simmer for about 15 minutes, then leave to cool.
2 Purée the raspberries with the lemon juice and pass through a fine sieve.
3 Mix the syrup with the raspberries and slowly pour in 300ml of the sparkling wine or Champagne.
4 Freeze in a shallow container, stirring with a fork every half an hour or so to stop crystals developing.
5 Serve with the remaining sparkling wine poured over the sorbet.

Per serving: Cals **322** Fat **0.5g** Sat fat **0g** Protein **1g**

time for action

beat the bulge with this eight-week cardio plan for all levels

The intensity of each workout is based on a scale of 0% (minimal effort) to 100% (maximum effort). Up the intensity of a session by increasing the speed or level, or adding extra hills or sprints. 'Exercises' refers to the toning moves from page 125.

week 1

MONDAY
RUN/JOG
All levels: 10 mins at 65%, then:
Beginner: 5 mins at 75%, 5 mins at 65%, 5 mins at 80%, 5 mins at 70%
Intermediate: 7 mins at 75%, 7 mins at 65%, 7 mins at 80%, 7 mins at 70%
Advanced: 7 mins at 80%, 7 mins at 70%, 7 mins at 85%, 7 mins at 70%
All levels: 4 exercises

TUESDAY
REST

WEDNESDAY
CYCLE
All levels: 10 mins at 65%, then:
30 secs at 90%, 2 mins 30 secs at 65%
Beginner: repeat x 6
Intermediate: repeat x 9
Advanced: repeat x 12
All levels: 10 mins at 60%, plus 4 exercises

THURSDAY
REST

FRIDAY
RUN/JOG
Beginner: 30 mins jog at 70%
Intermediate: 10 mins jog at 75%, 10 mins jog at 60%, 10 mins run at 75%
Advanced: 30 mins run at 80%
All levels: 4 exercises

SATURDAY
REST

SUNDAY
REST

week 2

MONDAY
RUN/JOG
Beginner: jog 1½km at 100%, 5 mins walk; repeat x 3, plus 4 exercises
Intermediate: jog/run 1½km fast at 100%, 4 mins walk; repeat x 3, plus 5 exercises
Advanced: run 2km at 100%, 4 mins walk/jog; repeat x 3, plus 6 exercises

TUESDAY
REST

WEDNESDAY
SWIM
All levels: 200m at 65%, then:
Beginner: 50m at 90%, 25m at 60%; repeat x 3
Intermediate: 50m at 95%, 25m at 65%; repeat x 4
Advanced: 50m at 100%, 25m at 65%; repeat x 5
All levels: 200m at 60%, then 5 exercises

THURSDAY
REST

FRIDAY
ANY CARDIO
Beginner: 1 min at 90%, 1 min at 60%; repeat x 15, plus 4 exercises
Intermediate: 1½ mins at 90%, 2 mins at 70%; repeat x 10, plus 5 exercises
Advanced: 2 mins at 100%, 1½ mins at 70%; repeat x 10, plus 6 exercises

SATURDAY
REST

SUNDAY
REST

week 3

MONDAY
ANY CARDIO
All levels: 20 mins at 70%
ROW
Beginner: 2,000m as quickly as possible and record time; plus 4 exercises
Intermediate: 2,500m as quickly as possible and record time; plus 5 exercises
Advanced: 3,000m as quickly as possible and record time; plus 6 exercises

TUESDAY
REST

WEDNESDAY
ANY CARDIO
All levels: 10 mins at 60%, then:
5 mins at 80%, 1 min at 100%
Beginner: repeat x 2
Intermediate: repeat x 3
Advanced: repeat x 5
All levels: 5 mins at 60%, 2 mins at 90%, 1 min at 70%
Beginner: repeat x 2
Intermediate: repeat x 3
Advanced: repeat x 4
All levels: 5 mins at 60%; plus 4 exercises

THURSDAY
REST

FRIDAY
CYCLE
All levels: 10 mins at 65%
Beginner: 5 mins hill climb at 85%, 2 mins at 60%, 2 mins sprint at 90%, 1 min at 60%; repeat x 3, plus 4 exercises
Intermediate: 6 mins hill climb at 85%, 2 mins at 65%, 2½ mins sprint at 90%, 1 min at 65%; repeat x 3, plus 5 exercises
Advanced: 6 mins hill climb at 85%, 2 mins at 65%, 2½ mins sprint at 90%, 1 min at 65%, 3 mins hill climb at 90%, 1 min at 60%; repeat x 3, plus 6 exercises

SATURDAY
ANY CARDIO
All levels: 30 mins at 70%

SUNDAY
REST

week 4

MONDAY
SWIM
All levels: 200m at 70%, then:
50m at 80%, 25m at 60%
Beginner: repeat x 4
Intermediate: repeat x 6
Advanced: repeat x 8
All levels: 200m at 60%, then:
25m at 100%, 25m at 60%
Beginner: repeat x 2; plus 5 exercises
Intermediate: repeat x 3; plus 6 exercises
Advanced: repeat x 4; plus 7 exercises

TUESDAY
REST

WEDNESDAY
ANY CARDIO
All levels: 20 mins at 70%
ROW
Beginner: 2,000m as quickly as possible and record time; plus 4 exercises
Intermediate: 2,500m as quickly as possible and record time; plus 5 exercises
Advanced: 3,000m as quickly as possible and record time; plus 6 exercises
ANY CARDIO
All levels: 10 mins at 70%, then:
Beginner: 5 exercises
Intermediate: 6 exercises
Advanced: 7 exercises

THURSDAY
REST

FRIDAY
ANY CARDIO
All levels: 30 mins at 70%; plus 5 exercises

SATURDAY
RUN/JOG
3 mins hill at 80%, 2 mins recovery at 50%, 2 mins run at 85%, 1 min at 55%
Beginner: repeat x 4
Intermediate: repeat x 5
Advanced: repeat x 6

week 5

MONDAY
CYCLE
All levels: 10 mins at 65%
Beginner: 5 mins hill climb (2 mins at 75%, 3 mins at 85%), 2 mins at 60%, 2½ mins sprint at 90%, then 1 min at 60%; repeat x 3, plus 5 exercises
Intermediate: 6 mins hill climb (3 mins at 80%, 3 mins at 85%), 1 min at 65%, 2½ mins sprint at 90%, 1 min at 65%; repeat x 3, plus 6 exercises
Advanced: 7 mins hill climb (3½ mins at 80%, 3½ mins at 85%), 1 min at 65%, 2½ mins sprint at 90%, 3 mins hill climb at 90%, 1 min at 60%; repeat x 3, plus 7 exercises

TUESDAY
REST

WEDNESDAY
SWIM
All levels: 200m at 75%, then:
25m at 90%, 25m at 80%
Beginner: repeat x 6
Intermediate: repeat x 8
Advanced: repeat x 10
All levels: 50m at 85%, 100m at 65%
Beginner: repeat x 3; plus 6 exercises
Intermediate: repeat x 4; plus 6 exercises
Advanced: repeat x 5; plus 6 exercises

THURSDAY
ANY CARDIO
All levels: 5 mins at 75%, 10 mins at 80%, 5 mins at 85%, 5 mins at 90%, 10 mins at 80%, 5 mins at 75%

FRIDAY
REST

SATURDAY
ROW
Beginner: 2,000m at 100% and record time; plus 5 exercises
Intermediate: 2,500m at 100% and record time; plus 6 exercises
Advanced: 3,000m at 100% and record time; plus 7 exercises
ANY CARDIO
All levels: 20 mins at 70%

SUNDAY
REST

week 6

MONDAY
ANY CARDIO
All levels: 45 mins at 70%
Beginner: 5 exercises
Intermediate: 6 exercises
Advanced: 7 exercises

TUESDAY
REST

WEDNESDAY
ANY CARDIO
All levels: 15 mins at 70%
ROW
500m at 100%, 1 min rest
Beginner: repeat x 3
Intermediate: repeat x 4
Advanced: repeat x 5
ANY CARDIO
All levels: 15 mins at 70%; plus 6 exercises

THURSDAY
REST

FRIDAY
SWIM
All levels: 200m at 70%, then:
50m at 80%, 25m at 60%
Beginners: repeat x 5
Intermediate: repeat x 7
Advanced: repeat x 10
All levels: 200m at 60%, then:
25m at 100%, 25m at 60%
Beginner: repeat x 3; plus 5 exercises
Intermediate: repeat x 4; then 6 exercises
Advanced: repeat x 5; then 7 exercises

SATURDAY
RUN/JOG
40 mins increasing speed:
Beginner: every 8 mins
Intermediate: every 6½ mins
Advanced: every 5 mins

SUNDAY
REST

week 7

MONDAY
RUN
Beginner: 500m at 75%, 500m at 85%, 700m at 60%; repeat x 3, plus 5 exercises
Intermediate: 500m at 75%, 500m at 90%, 800m at 60%; repeat x 4
Advanced: 500m at 75%, 500m at 90%, 1km at 60%; repeat x 5
All levels: 15 mins at 75%
Beginner: 5 exercises
Intermediate: 6 exercises
Advanced: 7 exercises

TUESDAY
REST

WEDNESDAY
CYCLE
All levels: 20 mins at 70%, then: 4 mins hill climb at 90%, 1 min sprint at 100%, 3 mins at 60%
Beginner: repeat x 3
Intermediate: repeat x 4
Advanced: repeat x 5
All levels: 10 mins at 70%
Beginner: 5 exercises
Intermediate: 6 exercises
Advanced: 7 exercises

THURSDAY
REST

FRIDAY
CYCLE
Beginner: 4 mins hill climb at 85%, 1 min sprint at 100%, 3 mins at 60%; repeat x 3 then 20 mins at 70%; plus 5 exercises
Intermediate: 5 mins hill climb at 85%, 1½ mins sprint at 100%, 3 mins at 60%; repeat x 4 then 25 mins at 70%; plus 6 exercises

Advanced: 5 mins hill climb at 90%, 2 mins sprint at 100%, 3 mins at 65%; repeat x 5, then 25 mins at 80%; plus 7 exercises

SATURDAY
ANY CARDIO
All levels: 40 mins starting at 60% and increasing the intensity by 5% every 5 mins

SUNDAY
REST

week 8

MONDAY
ANY CARDIO
All levels: 15 mins at 70%
ROW
500m as fast as possible then rest 1 min
Beginner: repeat x 3
Intermediate: repeat x 4
Advanced: repeat x 5
ANY CARDIO
All levels: 15 mins starting at 70% and increasing the intensity by 5% every 5 mins; then 7 exercises

TUESDAY
REST

WEDNESDAY
SWIM
All levels: 200m at 75%; then: 100m at 90%, 50m at 60%
Beginner: repeat x 3
Intermediate: repeat x 4
Advanced: repeat x 5
All levels: 200m at 75%, then: 25m at 100%, 25m at 60%
Beginners: repeat x 4; plus 5 exercises
Intermediate: repeat x 5; plus 6 exercises
Advanced: repeat x 6; plus 7 exercises

THURSDAY
ANY CARDIO
All levels: 45 mins starting at 60% and increasing the intensity by 5% every 5 mins

FRIDAY
REST

SATURDAY
RUN/JOG
Beginners: 5 mins hill at 80%, 1 min run at 90%, 3 mins run at 70%; repeat x 4, plus 5 exercises
Intermediate: 5 mins hill at 85%, 1½ mins run at 95%, 3 mins run at 75%; repeat x 5, plus 6 exercises
Advanced: 6 mins hill at 85%, 2 mins run at 95%, 3 mins run at 75%; repeat x 6, plus 7 exercises

SUNDAY
REST

bye bye trouble spots!

EQUIPMENT YOU'LL NEED
Stability ball
Weighted bar
Foam roller
Exercise mat
Balance pad/air disc
Medicine ball

blast fat and tone up your wobbly bits in eight quick and easy moves

Some people attribute their trouble spots to hormones and others blame their genes, but, whatever the reason, it's clear that women are prone to storing fat in certain areas around the body. While we can't burn fat with toning exercises alone, working out with resistance will help to tone and tighten troublesome areas. It will also help to increase lean muscle mass, which leads to a higher calorie burn overall.

how to do it

Do all these exercises in one workout by performing the prescribed number of reps and sets for your level twice a week for best results. Or, use the exercises in conjunction with the cardio plan from page 121.

01 ROLLER FRENCH PRESS

Beginner: 2 x 10 reps
Intermediate: 2 x 15 reps
Advanced: 3 x 15 reps

Trouble spot trained: Flabby arms
Technique:
■ Lie with a foam roller under your back, holding a weighted bar above your shoulders. This is the start position.
■ With your upper arms still, bend your elbows to 90 degrees, lowering the bar down close to your forehead.
■ Raise up again to the start position and repeat.
Tip: If you want to increase the challenge to your core, lift one leg off the floor.

02 SIDE CRUNCH

Beginner: 2 x 10 reps (each side)
Intermediate: 2 x 12 reps (each side)
Advanced: 3 x 12 reps (each side)

Trouble spot trained: Love handles
Technique:
■ Anchor your feet against a wall with your right foot behind, left foot in front, and rest your left side on a stability ball.
■ Place your arms across your chest or hands at your temples (to increase difficulty) and lower yourself over the ball, bending from the waist.
■ Lift your upper body back to the start, without rotating your upper body, and repeat to complete one set.

03 FRONT SQUAT

Beginner: 2 x 10 reps
Intermediate: 2 x 12 reps
Advanced: 3 x 12 reps

Trouble spot trained:
Chunky thighs
Technique:
■ Place a weighted bar across your shoulders, holding it in place with arms crossed, your feet shoulder-width apart or slightly wider and toes turned out slightly. This is the start position.
■ Without leaning forwards, bend your hips and knees, squatting down until your hips are level with your knees.
■ Push through your heels, return to the start position and repeat.

04 HUNDRED

Beginner: 1 set
Intermediate: 2 sets
Advanced: 3 sets

Trouble spot trained:
Flabby tummy
Technique:
■ Sit tall with knees slightly bent and feet on the ground.
■ Extend your arms forward, level with your chest with palms facing down, and lean back to around 45 degrees (the further you lean back, the harder the exercise).
■ Lift your feet off the floor and pulse your arms up and down (roughly one inch). Count to 100 at double time to complete one set, breathing out for five counts and in for five counts.

For more training tips, workouts and the latest fitness news, visit our website at womensfitness. co.uk

05 MEDICINE BALL PULLOVER

Beginner: 2 x 10 reps
Intermediate: 2 x 12 reps
Advanced: 3 x 12 reps

Trouble spot trained: Back fat
Technique:

■ Sit on a stability ball, holding a medicine ball in both hands, and walk your feet forward until only your head and upper back are supported, with your knees bent at 90 degrees.
■ Extend your arms straight out behind you, in line with your body, with your upper arms close to your ears. This is the start position.
■ Keeping your stomach tight, lift the medicine ball until it's directly over your chest, keeping your arms straight.
■ Slowly lower your arms to the start position and repeat to complete one set.

06 CALF RAISE

Beginner: 2 x 10 reps
Intermediate: 2 x 12 reps
Advanced: 3 x 12 reps

Trouble spot trained:
Chunky calves
Technique:

■ Stand with your feet hip-width apart, your right foot on a balance pad or air disc, your left foot on the floor and your hands on your hips.
■ Raise your left foot off the floor, holding a wall for support with your right hand if needed.
■ Rise onto the ball of your right foot, lower and repeat to complete one set, then repeat on the left foot.

07 SIDE KICK

Beginner: 1 x 25 reps (each leg)
Intermediate: 2 x 25 reps (each leg)
Advanced: 2 x 30 reps (each leg)

Trouble spot trained: Saggy bottom
Technique:
■ Kneel with your knees directly underneath your hips, right forearm and left hand on the floor under your shoulders. This is the start position.
■ Lift your left leg and cross it behind your right leg, keeping your knee bent and toe pointed.
■ Shift your weight over to your right, straightening your left arm slightly, taking your left leg up and out to hip level and slowly kicking, straightening your knee.
■ Repeat to finish set then change legs.

08 OFFSET PUSH-UP

Beginner: 2 x 10 reps (each arm)
Intermediate: 2 x 12 reps (each arm)
Advanced: 3 x 12 reps (each arm)

Trouble spot trained: Saggy bust
Technique:

■ Start in a push-up position with hands slightly wider than shoulder-width apart, resting on either your toes or knees.
■ Walk your left hand out to the side slightly so that your hands are in a staggered position.
■ Bend your elbows and lower your chest as close to the floor as you can.
■ Push back to the start position and repeat to complete one set, switching arms for the next set.

recipe index

⟶